The Executive Guide to Understanding and Implementing Quality Cost Programs

Also available from ASQ Quality Press:

The Executive Guide to Understanding and Implementing the Baldrige Criteria: Improve Revenue and Create Organizational Excellence
Denis Leonard and Mac McGuire

The Executive Guide to Understanding and Implementing Employee Engagement Programs: Expand Capacity, Increase Revenue, and Save Jobs
Pat Townsend and Joan Gebhardt

The Executive Guide to Understanding and Implementing Lean Six Sigma: The Financial Impact
Robert M. Meisel, Steven J. Babb, Steven F. Marsh, and James P. Schlichting

Principles of Quality Costs: Principles, Implementation, and Use, Third Edition
Jack Campanella, editor

The Certified Manager of Quality/Organizational Excellence Handbook, Third Edition
Russell T. Westcott, editor

The Quality Improvement Handbook, Second Edition
ASQ Quality Management Division and John E. Bauer, Grace L. Duffy, and Russell T. Westcott, editors

The Executive Guide to Improvement and Change
G. Dennis Beecroft, Grace L. Duffy, and John W. Moran

Simplified Project Management for the Quality Professional: Managing Small and Medium-Size Projects
Russell T. Westcott

Avoiding the Corporate Death Spiral: Recognizing and Eliminating the Signs of Decline
Gregg Stocker

The Path to Profitable Measures: 10 Steps to Feedback That Fuels Performance
Mark W. Morgan

Quality Essentials: A Reference Guide from A to Z
Jack B. ReVelle

Quality management—Guidelines for realizing financial and economic benefits
ANSI/ISO/ASQ Q10014-2006

To request a complimentary catalog of ASQ Quality Press publications, call 800-248-1946, or visit our Web site at http://qualitypress.asq.org.

The Executive Guide to Understanding and Implementing Quality Cost Programs

Reduce Operating Expenses and Increase Revenue

The ASQ Quality Management Division
Economics of Quality Book Series

Douglas C. Wood

ASQ Quality Press
Milwaukee, Wisconsin

American Society for Quality, Quality Press, Milwaukee 53203
© 2007 by ASQ
All rights reserved. Published 2007
Printed in the United States of America
13 12 11 10 09 08 07   5 4 3 2 1

Library of Congress Cataloging-in-Publication Data

Wood, Douglas C., 1955–
The executive guide to understanding and implementing quality cost programs : reduce operating expenses and increase revenue / Douglas C. Wood.
    p. cm.—(The ASQ quality management division economics of quality book series)
    Includes bibliographical references and index.
    ISBN 978-0-87389-716-7 (soft cover : alk. paper)
    1. Cost control. 2. Quality control. I. Title.

    HD47.3.W67 2007
    658.15'52—dc22   2007021341

ISBN: 978-0-87389-716-7

Publisher: William A. Tony
Acquisitions Editor: Matt T. Meinholz
Project Editor: Paul O'Mara
Production Administrator: Randall Benson

ASQ Mission: The American Society for Quality advances individual, organizational, and community excellence worldwide through learning, quality improvement, and knowledge exchange.

Attention Bookstores, Wholesalers, Schools, and Corporations: ASQ Quality Press books, videotapes, audiotapes, and software are available at quantity discounts with bulk purchases for business, educational, or instructional use. For information, please contact ASQ Quality Press at 800-248-1946, or write to ASQ Quality Press, P.O. Box 3005, Milwaukee, WI 53201-3005.

To place orders or to request a free copy of the ASQ Quality Press Publications Catalog, including ASQ membership information, call 800-248-1946. Visit our Web site at www.asq.org or http://www.asq.org/quality-press.

Printed in the United States of America

 Printed on acid-free paper

Quality Press
600 N. Plankinton Avenue
Milwaukee, Wisconsin 53203
Call toll free 800-248-1946
Fax 414-272-1734
www.asq.org
http://www.asq.org/quality-press
http://standardsgroup.asq.org
E-mail: authors@asq.org

To Marilyn
for helping me keep my face to the music.

Table of Contents

Part I   Executive Overview

List of Figures and Tables

Introduction

If, as it is often said, we are what we eat, then it may follow that we are also what we read. If nothing else, books that broaden our knowledge are indeed food for the brain.

That is the purpose of The ASQ Quality Management Division's book series on the economics of quality—to stimulate thought on how different quality methods can be used to influence the financial position of an organization.

A manager may want to know about a popular business topic, an engineer responsible for cost control may need a good business tool, or a person new to the quality profession wants to understand more about the many different approaches that drive organizational success; what we all seek are answers to two simple questions, What is it? and How do I get started? This book series has those answers.

The Economics of Quality Book Series is written by subject matter experts from business, academia, consulting, and not-for-profit organizations. They represent the best minds on the subject about which they write.

This series is not intended to be a collection of application guides. It is introductory material to point us in the right direction so we know what the capabilities of a method are. These books are intended to arm us with the right questions so that if we want to deploy a particular methodology, we know what to ask in order to move to the next step in the implementation process.

The subject matter experts of the Quality Management Division are members of a variety of Technical Committees who have specific and in-depth knowledge about methods such as Baldrige, ISO, Lean Six Sigma, quality costs, employee involvement, quality management information systems, globalization/supply chain, data-driven decision making, and quality in project management.

In addition to sharing their expertise through books like this one, the committees contribute to business journals and speak at quality and business conferences.

You can find out more about the Quality Management Division through the American Society for Quality Web site: www.asq.org. As a member of the Society and Division you will benefit from the professional contributions of our technical committees and other subject matter experts. The Division publishes a peer-reviewed journal, *The Forum,* that provides in-depth application guidance to improving all types of organizations. As a member you will also have the opportunity to attend our annual conference dedicated to quality and organizational improvement. Our goal is to help make all organizations, and broader society, a better place to work and live.

William H. Denney, PhD
Vice Chair, Technical Committees
Quality Management Division
American Society for Quality

Preface

This work on cost of quality methods is part of the ASQ Quality Management Division's Economics of Quality Book Series, a collection of organizational improvement approaches that apply to all market sectors and all types of organizations. This book is intended to provide a fundamental introduction to *cost of quality* concepts (often simply referred to as *quality costs*) for executives or those individuals new to quality concepts. In addition, it can help anyone in an organization interested in how this measurement methodology links to business costs. This book is not intended to be used as a handbook or as an in-depth exploration of the underlying methodology, but rather as a helpful overview of an approach to maximize value and bottom-line impact.

The book has two purposes. In Part I (Chapters 1 through 3), executives can quickly learn the key components of cost of quality. Chapter 1 covers basic principles, Chapter 2 looks at organization and other implementation factors, and Chapter 3 provides an overview of cost of quality measurement.

In Part II (Chapters 4 through 6), implementers can find some of the details of building a cost of quality measure. Chapter 4 contains process details, Chapter 5 has recommendations on how to sell a cost of quality program, and Chapter 6 discusses pitfalls.

Both manufacturing and nonmanufacturing firms who are contemplating or just getting started on a quality cost measurement program will find this book especially valuable. To aid in illustrating the application of these principles to diverse and global businesses, case studies have been selected and included to demonstrate how the general approach can accommodate and enhance different types of organizations. These examples demonstrate the broad spectrum across which quality cost methods can be used as a measurement tool, making improved performance clear in a dollars-and-cents manner.

I hope you find this overview of quality costs enjoyable and informative, and I wish you success on the execution of your implementation.

Douglas C. Wood

Acknowledgments

Agreat many people helped make this book a reality. I would like to thank all of them here, but I probably will miss someone. If so, I hope a general "thanks to everyone else" will suffice.

Among those whom I can recall by name, thanks to William H. Denney for his editing expertise (and so much else), Heather McCain and Lois Cowden, friends who have provided much, along with Gary Cokins, Jack Campanella, Suhansa Rodchua, Dennis Beecroft, Grace Duffy, Jd Marhevko, Art Trepanier, Noel Wilson, Susanne Donovan, Dean Bottorff, H. Fred Walker, John Schottmiller, and the helpful people at ASQ Quality Press.

Finally, thanks to my family, who have supported me as this work has continued: Marilyn, Chris, and Jenny.

Part I

Executive Overview

1

Cost of Quality Core Principles

Understanding the cost of quality (the overall costs of producing a quality product) is one of the oldest quality business methods. The roots go back to 1951, when Dr. J. M. Juran's first *Quality Control Handbook* made the analogy of "gold in the mine."[1] That is, there are often hidden costs we can't see but which can be recovered. Other publications adding to an understanding of quality costs included Dr. A. V. Feigenbaum's book, *Total Quality Control.*

DEFINITIONS

Quality costs are the costs connected with both attaining and missing the desired level of quality in a service or product. They may be seen as the costs of preventing quality problems, measuring quality levels, controlling and/or inspecting quality levels, or failing to accomplish the desired quality levels.

In *Principles of Quality Costs,* Jack Campanella defined them as:

The difference between the actual cost of a product or service, and what the reduced cost would be if there was no possibility of substandard service, failure of products, or defects in their manufacture.[2]

QUALITY COST CATEGORIES

Over the last several decades, quality costs have been divided into several categories. The most commonly accepted and comprehensive definitions have categorized quality costs as 1) prevention, 2) appraisal, and 3) failure costs. Failure costs are usually split into internal failure costs and external failure costs. Here are the definitions of these terms from *Principles of Quality Costs.*

prevention costs—Costs of all activities specifically designed to prevent poor quality in products or services. Examples are the costs of new product review, quality planning, supplier capability surveys, process capability evaluations, quality improvement team meetings, quality improvement projects, quality education and training.

appraisal costs—Costs associated with measuring, evaluating, or auditing products or services to assure conformance to quality standards and performance requirements. These include the costs of incoming and source inspection/test of purchased material, in-process and final inspection/test, product, process, or service audits, calibration of measuring and test equipment, and the costs of associated supplies and materials.

failure costs—Costs resulting from products or services not conforming to requirements or customer/user needs. Failure costs are divided into internal and external failure cost categories.[3]

Failure costs are usually split into two categories. The division occurs where the product or service leaves the organization's control.

internal failure costs—Failure costs occurring prior to delivery or shipment of the product, or the furnishing of a service, to the customer. Examples are the costs of scrap, rework, reinspection, retesting, material review, and downgrading.

external failure costs—Failure costs occurring after delivery or shipment of the product, and during or after furnishing of a service, to the customer. Examples are the costs of processing customer complaints, customer returns, warranty claims, and product recalls.[4]

The total of these costs defines quality costs in the broadest sense. Some authors choose to use only portions of these costs when suggesting quality cost approaches. The choice of including or excluding these costs will lie within your organization, so all of these will be discussed here. See Appendix A for a more complete list of the elements of these categories. As you will see, the total list of potential quality costs can be exhaustive and create its own financial exercise. It is recommended that when establishing a quality cost tracking system, the implementer use the Pareto method to identify the highest loss contributors. Track these loss and/or cost areas, improve them, and use the quality cost report to measure the level of improvement. As improvement diminishes, add the secondary quality costs and repeat the improvement process.

THE GOAL OF A QUALITY COST SYSTEM

Improving the bottom line is the goal. While preventive costs may increase, overall operational cost will decrease through the reduction of failures. A properly understood and managed quality cost system will aid organizations in realizing cost savings while avoiding some of the serious pitfalls that can accompany cost cutting: decreases in product or service quality, increased customer dissatisfaction, added rework costs, or simple shifts in costs from one area to another.

The central idea behind cost of quality systems is that the largest quality costs occur after product has shipped or a service has been performed, that is, external failure costs. Altering activities and focusing efforts so that quality issues are identified in progressively earlier stages of internal failure (before shipment), appraisal, and prevention will reduce overall organizational costs. Reducing quality costs is also considered an effective way to regain margin.

A second idea is that while external failure costs are often larger than costs created earlier in the flow, they can also be harder to measure or tie to causal events. Warranty costs, for example, are usually easy to measure, but it may be difficult to identify how the problem found by a customer and paid for in a warranty claim was caused in the manufacturing or procurement process. In addition, costs due to lost sales are very difficult to quantify. Knowing what these costs are and doing something about them may be difficult if you start with the external costs.

One approach is to start with those internal failure costs that you can identify and tie to specific work activities. While this may seem to be a roundabout approach to addressing those significant external failure costs, it is often much simpler; for in most cases, the roots that underlie these internal failure cost–generating activities are tied to those (much larger) external failure costs. So by eliminating the root causes internally, all quality costs are reduced.

Installing and using a quality cost program will allow leadership to make a guided transition from an organization's current operational costs to a state of minimal quality costs. At the same time, reducing problems found by the customer is one way to enhance revenue via retention of sales.

There are two significant aspects in looking at quality costs. First, the cost of quality for a given issue grows larger as the product moves toward the customer. From design, to initial production setup, to full production, to distribution, to the customer's location, and finally to possible litigation, each step can result in a tenfold increase in quality costs. Not all issues make it to the last stage, but all increase in cost as they move forward. See Figure 1.1.

Second, most quality costs are not obvious and open. These are called hidden quality costs, and they are often many times the size of the easily measured costs. The iceberg analogy is useful here. Many organizations tend to measure only the tip of the iceberg while the real costs of poor quality in operations and delivery of a product or service lie below the surface. In Figure 1.2, the total cost of quality encompasses the entire iceberg.

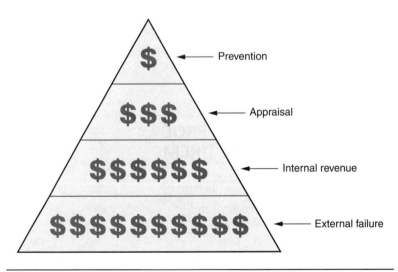

Figure 1.1   Relative magnitudes of quality cost categories.

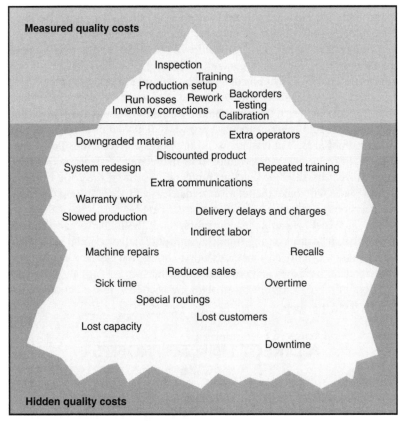

Figure 1.2   The iceberg of measured and hidden quality costs.

THE NEED FOR A PRODUCT/SERVICE QUALITY MEASUREMENT SYSTEM

Most measurement systems at the topmost levels of an organization revolve around financials. This is driven by the rules of commerce and investment, tax regulations, and tradition. On the other hand, where products are actually created or service transactions are completed, measurement is rarely monetary. At this level, parts, transactions, *things* are measured. A transaction can be good or bad, meet the customer requirements or fail to meet expectations. Traditionally, most quality measures focus on counting up the good and bad and applying some kind of ratio to determine the relative 'goodness' or 'badness' of an operation.

Simply measuring 'good' or 'bad' will not make the financial impact of quality issues clear to an organization's strategic planners. While a product/service quality measurement system is required to get at the root activities or causes of quality issues, these measurement systems report data from inspections, tests, process control variables, reasons for production loss, quality audits, and customer complaints. This detail is important in the operations areas, but it is not useful in prioritizing resource allocations. Such quality measures alone cannot show the relative strategic and/or economic impact of different kinds of problems. However, the costs of those quality issues will make the relative needs clear and allow resource allocation decisions to solve the most severe issues first.

Quality cost measurement, therefore, takes the higher organizational perspective. It focuses on the financial impact of activities related to good or bad quality. Quality cost methods help to bridge the gap between higher-level financial measures and production-level measures.

Both of these measurement systems are needed to direct action across the entire organization.

A DIRECT LINK TO PROFITS

Well-intentioned organizational improvement may merely reorganize or shift costs from one area to another. Manufacturing 'fixes' could increase packing costs. Product redesign changes may cause production waste. Since every dollar of quality cost reductions is directly added to profits, the benefits of measuring quality costs across a business system are clear. Additionally, an organizational approach to reduce quality costs can provide an increased quality level at the same or lower cost. Finally, the added benefit of improved quality is increased revenue when improved quality is perceived by the customer as increased value and marginal income is derived from that customer perception.

THE NATURE OF A QUALITY COST SYSTEM

Establishing a quality cost system usually does not require extensive accounting system changes. Most accounting systems in use today collect more data than is reported. Access to detailed data currently available may provide enough information to set up a quality cost program. Reporting this detail in the form of quality costs can be done with many existing financial systems.

On occasion, however, the existing accounting system is outdated or lacks the detail necessary for separating costs into the various quality cost areas. In these cases a small addition to the existing system may be needed. It is almost always true that the existing accounting reports will not clearly show the effect of quality on the organization's operating costs. This is because the focus of normal accounting reports does not highlight quality costs and their cause-and-effect nature.

For example, a normal accounting system would usually identify costs by department, or by product. What would not be visible is the cost of pre-production planning by a central engineering department. Also, this cost would not be compared to the inspection costs by product type and the failure costs by product type. There is nothing missing from the normal accounting reports, but the costs are simply not compiled to show prevention, appraisal, and failure cost relationships for various product types.

The key to an effective quality cost system is to strike a balance between practicality and comprehensiveness. Using the best aspects of the existing accounting system will limit data collection costs. If the larger elements of quality cost are not identified by the existing accounting system, some form of estimation may be needed at first. The critical need is to make sure that the quality cost data makes sense to management, that is, it covers all the known and/or expected sources of quality cost. During the setup of a quality cost system there may need to be some trials to establish the key sources.

However, a successful cost of quality program should be comprehensive and not just cover those portions of the business (or cost areas) that are simple or obvious. Leaving out portions that are significant but difficult to obtain will skew the decisions and approaches taken to reduce costs. This could introduce many more issues than it will solve. For example, ignoring customer complaint costs is likely to discourage a link between specific prevention activities and the major customer complaints. Without the correct prevention actions, customer complaints are not likely to diminish until the organization has lost the complaining customers.

The cost of quality approach and its measurements should be viewed as behavior modification tools. The goal is to change the behavior of the organization's employees as a group. While it is financial in nature, cost of quality is not a comprehensive accounting measure. What senior managers expect from an accounting group are reports that measure the totality of costs within a particular area. Quality costs do not measure all the costs in any one area; rather, they measure costs that can be linked together to reinforce the proper organizational behavior.

To some, the above distinction is used as a criticism of quality cost programs: a quality cost program does not measure all the organization's costs, so it cannot be as effective as a broad-spectrum cost-reduction effort. However, an across-the-board effort is not as likely to identify cause-and-effect relationships as a quality cost program. Reducing prevention efforts when significant existing costs arise from lack of prevention is not likely to help an organization achieve sustainability.

There are many approaches to manager or employee behavior modification. One such approach might be an organizational goal to find X number of raw material suppliers. If this goal is listed in the performance objectives of executives who make sourcing decisions, their behavior in choosing suppliers is likely to change.

A quality cost program changes behaviors by:

- Highlighting the costs of issues that may have been hidden in the overall accounting totals

- Linking the costs of such issues (both the cost of measurement and the actual costs themselves) to specific prevention activities, even if those activities are outside the particular organizational silo where the costs occur (or are identified)

- Increasing prevention activities tied to particular quality issues

- Measuring the effectiveness of changes and making further corrections

If a business has the objective to reduce overall organizational costs, then the major elements of quality cost must be easily visible to key managers. If major quality cost elements are left buried in accounts with other costs, management action to improve operations and quality may be missing, misguided, or too limited in scope.

BASES AND RATIOS

Quality costs are more than just a variant of product costs or organization expenses in general. However, the simplest view is that the lower the cost of quality, the better. For an organization that is new to quality cost measurements, this approach may lead to initial short-term improvements. Soon, however, the nature of normal variability arises and cost of quality will go up and down. These variations are often due to changes in production volume. The solution is to make the cost of quality measure a ratio to some normal production volume measure.

Here is an example of how just looking at costs may not establish a clear direction. If just the costs of quality were charted, it might look like Figure 1.3.

It is hard to see a trend from Figure 1.3. Suppose that sales have been decreasing steadily over this five-month period. Figure 1.4 shows the same costs, but with a ratio of quality cost to sales added to show the trend.

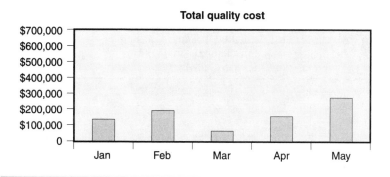

Figure 1.3 Quality costs trend chart.

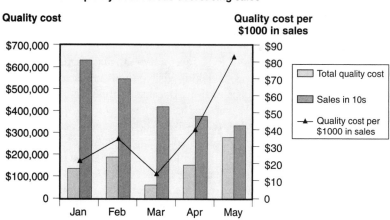

Figure 1.4 Quality costs trend with decreasing sales.

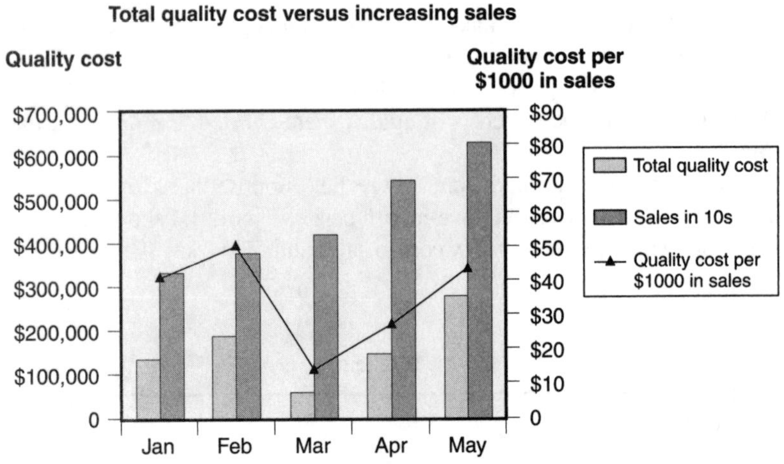

Total quality cost versus increasing sales

Figure 1.5 Quality costs trend with increasing sales.

Clearly, the quality cost per $1000 in sales shows a poor direction. Now, if the sales had been increasing over the same time period, the picture would look like Figure 1.5.

Figure 1.5 shows a positive trend or at least one where the costs of quality have been held steady.

Choosing a base for the ratio may be a difficult task. For longer-range comparisons, net sales or cost of goods sold are often used. For shorter-range comparisons (monthly for example), something closer to the generation of the costs is needed. Here is where things can become difficult. Table 1.1 shows several choices and their pros and cons.

Most likely there will need to be several bases to make actual improvement (or decline) in the costs of quality visible to all levels of an organization and over different spans of time. Because of this, there is a critical need to understand how the various bases change with respect to each other. Without this knowledge, there will be disagreement between managers who rely on the different ratios. For example, if cost of quality over net sales shows an improvement (measure A) while the same quality costs over units produced (measure B) show a decline, senior leaders focusing on measure A will be under the impression that operations are going well (see Figure 1.6). The production managers using measure B will be faced with a decline in performance and will not be able to communicate the urgency

Table 1.1　Pros and cons of volumetric bases.

Base	Pro	Con
Net sales	Well understood by senior leaders	Variations may be nonsynchronous with costs of quality
Cost of goods sold	Closer to margin gain opportunity	Administrative costs may remain stable while quality costs change
Cost of goods produced	Primary area of concentration for initial quality cost program	Overhead costs may remain stable while quality costs change
Prime cost	Well known by managers	Only direct expense is included (small portion of expenses)
Labor costs	Simple to measure and understand	Labor reduction projects will show poorer cost of quality performance
Labor hours	Easy to understand in the factory	Labor reduction projects will show poorer cost of quality performance
Process or machine cycles	Tracks close to major failure costs	Affected by changes in type of products
Units produced	Easy to understand, directly related to process	Affected by changes in type of products

of the improvement program (see Figure 1.7). Both perceptions can be true if there is an understanding that the units being sold are not the same units being produced during the report period. It may also happen that the units being sold currently have a larger opportunity for costs of quality while the units sold in an earlier time period had a much smaller opportunity for costs of quality. The use of several bases and full understanding of the organizations' work mix, time lag, and their effects on measurements will help sort out this situation.

The use of different bases is a situation where tracking of additional data in the reporting may be helpful. Even if a particular base is not chosen for one year's reports, it may be desired in later reports. Having the data captured will aid in comparisons or analyses between the two time periods.

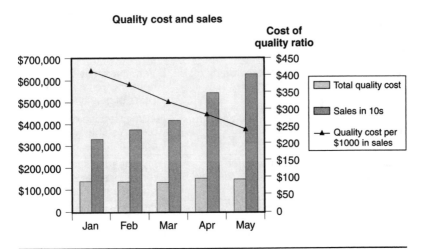

Figure 1.6   Improving cost of quality performance against increasing sales (measure A).

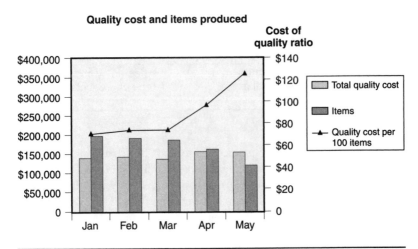

Figure 1.7   Declining cost of quality performance against smaller item production (measure B).

THE ROLE OF ACCOUNTING

All of the previous discussion indicates a major role in the quality cost system for the accounting or controller's office. It cannot be stressed enough that the overall responsibility for the collection of quality cost data, data transformations, and reporting must lie in the accounting department. Holding the controller responsible for operating the quality cost program will:

- Match quality cost definitions to other company cost structures

- Ensure that methods of estimating costs are sound

- Keep the quality cost system synchronous with other cost systems as changes are made

- Manage report production in an area that focuses on cost reporting

- Help establish an internal quality cost procedure that maintains year-to-year consistency

More importantly, running the quality cost program from the controller's office will:

- Provide the stamp of financial validity to the program.

- Assure that collection costs remain within practical limits.

- Set up a regular opportunity for dialogue between the controller, operations, and the traditional quality function. This will help put both the quality manager and the controller in the flow of communication to help the operations manager reduce the cost of quality.

While the accounting department may not (at first) wish to accept this task eagerly, the concept of linking quality measurements to costs does fit within the normal practice of using costs as primary decision drivers. It is hard to argue against the concept of reducing cost while at the same time improving quality. In the effort to convince the controller to use the accounting department to take on this measurement task we must remember that quality costs are a tool used to justify and measure key improvement actions, and insignificant activities may be left out of a quality cost system to ensure simplicity. So we want to measure those costs that can have significant impact on operational decisions.

It is important to emphasize to everyone involved that this isn't just a measurement exercise. In the words of Taiichi Ohno, "Costs do not exist to be calculated. Costs exist to be reduced."[5]

THE MANAGEMENT OF
QUALITY COSTS

There are two underpinning concepts that guide the management of quality costs:

- Achieving a higher level of product or service quality through process control will result in overall lower quality costs

- Improving product or service quality will also improve other organization measures (market share, customer satisfaction, customer retention, speed to market, and so on)

A common reaction to a quality issue is to add resources to compensate. For example, a sudden increase in calls to a service center may be handled by adding more service personnel. This actually increases external failure cost because handling complaints is part of the failure cost measurement. However, if the link to missing appraisal or prevention activities were made and those areas either increased or refocused, the entire cost of the quality issue would be removed—less appraisal cost, less internal failure cost, and less external failure cost would result. In addition, a refocusing of prevention activities would likely pay benefits on other seemingly unrelated issues. Problems that were not connected to the reported service center complaints would be identified and solved. Removing the causes of poor quality instead of increasing service staff would save money, reduce failures, and satisfy customers. See Figure 1.8.

In the example above, the action taken of increasing prevention and appraisal activity in the area identified by the service center problem was obvious because the quality cost system was built with linkages between the prevention, appraisal, and failure areas. This made the problem-solving process straightforward. Using a quality cost approach in this manner can be a powerful tool.

Six Sigma and DMAIC

To show how the Six Sigma improvement methodology's DMAIC (define, measure, analyze, improve, control) works with quality costs, consider the example from Figure 1.8 in this way:

Define. The problem is a surge in call center volume. The benefits are identified as both a return to the lower volume of call center calls as well as other organizational impacts due to the product issue.

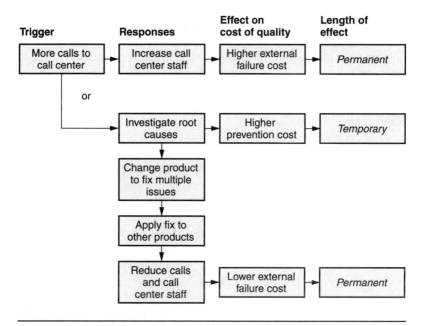

Figure 1.8   Two approaches to reducing quality costs.

Measure. Quality costs show the organizationwide impact in dollar terms of the increased call center volume and related product problems.

Analyze. Because the cost of quality program has been designed with cause-and-effect drivers, analysis is quick. The causes are identified, solutions are evaluated, and a corrective action is identified. The product corrections and resources to make systemic corrections are reflected as temporarily higher prevention costs. These costs (shown as Six Sigma project investments) are justified by the benefits defined and measured above.

Improve. Alterations are made in identified products, and in similar products, as well as systems when needed.

Control. Quality costs again help, this time measuring the effectiveness and sustainability of the improvements.

Having a quality cost system that shows detail by business area will show that different areas inherently need more or less prevention and appraisal activities to control their failure costs. Over time, the pace of improvement in each area will provide a gauge of the management health of these areas.

Comparison of the overall costs of quality in one business area to another is a poor practice. Each may be realistically compared to itself over time, but the comparison of different areas to each other only serves to highlight the differences in market or product. Such differences are not relevant to how each area is managed. Comparing an area to itself over time will avoid highlighting differences that do not reflect true management issues.

But comparing costs between departments is a different issue from seeing the linkage of costs between departments. The design of traditional cost systems usually does not allow linkage across departments. However, a well designed cost of quality measure should show the effects of problems in one department on another. An example would be a tooling group in a preproduction department that saves costs and reduces cycle time, but whose tools now produce a higher defect rate in the production department. If both departments are charged with reducing the cost of quality, a solution should be sought that optimizes costs for the entire organization.

Besides highlighting areas that need quality improvement, a cost of quality program can be used to measure the overall progress of an organization. Typical prevention measures also improve other organizational measures, but the connection can be difficult to see with a traditional accounting system. For example, labor efficiency is often reported in traditional cost accounting systems. A company showing improved labor efficiency may attribute the lower costs to better scheduling or running higher-efficiency machines. However, poor-quality prevention activities included in operator training on optimal machine setup methods may be the real reason for the higher run speed and better labor efficiency.

By looking at prevention, appraisal, and failure costs in different business areas, management can make better decisions to prioritize improvement activities. These decisions will be based on realistic financial data combined with the organization-relative knowledge that illustrates cause-and-effect linkages. The allocation of additional prevention activities or more engineering staff to an area that displays a large failure-to-prevention ratio makes good business sense. Simply because a business area has inherently large failure costs does not make it poorly managed, but it may make it one that needs greater prevention activities due to the nature of its operations. As mentioned before, those prevention activities may actually take place in an organizationally distant work area.

Look at a comparison between two organizational units. In year one, units A and B have a comparable ratio of failure costs to prevention costs. Unit A decides to increase their prevention expenses, raising their overall cost of quality temporarily. By closely focusing those added prevention activities on root causes and planning, unit A reduces their failure costs and overall cost of quality in year two. Unit B shows no real change, although their failure costs were reduced slightly due to focusing on employee training in established procedures.

In Figure 1.9, unit A has moved rapidly toward improvement, while unit B has changed little. Comparing the ratios of failure to prevention tells why.

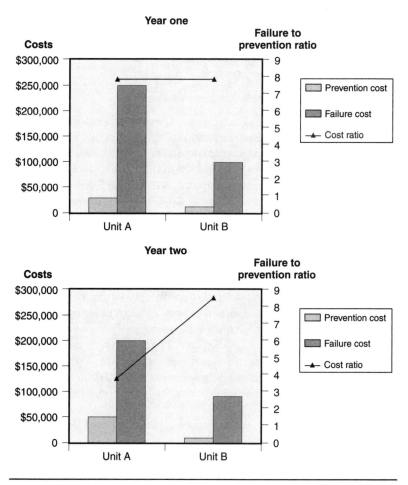

Figure 1.9   Two organizational units' prevention versus failure costs over time.

One of the best aspects of a cost of quality system is that it finally allows a payoff to be shown on quality activities. Quality may be free, as Philip Crosby said, but not showing the cost of good quality in comparison to the cost of poor quality (or the cost of conformance to the cost of non-conformance) makes business decisions more difficult. For example, after many improvement projects, senior managers may ask if there is a point of diminishing returns. In other words, has the organization reached the point where added improvement consumes more resources than it returns in benefits? A cost of quality program will answer that by showing the year-over-year pace of improvement.

STEPS IN MANAGING QUALITY COSTS

1. Reduce Failure Costs

Most organizations do this. The problem is, many organizations may just encourage employees to "do the right thing." If encouraging employees to reduce costs is the chosen action, it is not likely to produce ideal results. In any organization, you will be hard-pressed to find an employee that says as they start work, "I'm going to make poor quality today." All of us do the best we can within the process where we work. Encouraging better work in an ineffective process (or an efficient process that is linked to other inefficient processes) will have no real or lasting effect.

A way of linking causes to losses needs to be established for real improvement to begin. Most first-level managers will profess to know their number one quality problem. They are unlikely to know their number two quality problem or number three quality problem, however. A Pareto analysis, or cause tracking project, will make these clear. A cause tracking project may even identify that several of the lesser problems have the same causes and can be fixed with one effort. The total of several lesser problems may even have a higher cost than the one larger issue, so this approach can refocus improvement actions in a different direction than the first-level manager would have selected from the beginning. Think of this as deep-level cause identification.

Let's take a situation and follow the causes backward. We can then look for patterns in the causes.

In this example, back orders collect at a warehouse. Previous quality cost analyses show that these back orders cost $250 each and they occur 40 times per year. The cost is $10,000 per year, and management feels that this problem needs to be addressed. A group of employees is assembled and obvious first-level causes of the back orders are determined to be: lack of stock in the warehouse, lost/late order paperwork, and a shortage of loading docks. While these findings are helpful, going deeper and looking at the next couple of layers of causes yields the list below. In this list, each subsequent indent shows another deeper causal level:

Lack of stock in the warehouse

    Delayed production orders

        Changes in product specifications

        Production bottlenecks

        Raw material shortage

            Incorrect ordering of raw material

                Bad records in the records department

                    Records department staff turnover

    Unusually high demand for certain parts

        Seasonal peaks three times per year

        Unanticipated outside events—hurricane last year

    Missing stock

        Records not correct

            Records department staff turnover

        Materials incorrectly stored

            Warehouse too full

                Incorrect ordering of raw material

                    Bad records in the records department

                        Records department staff turnover

Lost/late order paperwork

    Backlogged filing in the records department

        Records department staff turnover

    Missing information in the order

        Training of new hires

Shortage of loading docks

Loading dock space limited by building layout

Peak demand three times per year

One dock/ trailer used as storage

Warehouse storage is full

Too much unneeded material

Incorrect ordering of raw material

Bad records in the records department

Records department staff turnover

One cause (records department staff turnover) shows up five times, affecting all three of the initially unrelated first-level causes. By tracking the root causes, common causes are uncovered. By working on the common causes, all the higher-level causes can be removed or their impact reduced.

Key finding: If the first-level causes had been attacked without a deeper understanding, effort would have been wasted in many areas and the improvement program may have been sidetracked before any benefit was established.

2. Evaluate Appraisal Costs

Perhaps too little is spent on measuring quality, compared to failure costs. Alternatively, appraisal costs may be coming from areas with limited failure costs. Quality cost measurement allows alignment of appraisal tasks with failure areas. This may mean raising, lowering, or simply reallocating inspection and testing activities.

Key finding: Allocation decisions for inspection and testing efforts need to be based on linkages to current internal and external failure costs.

3. Link Prevention Activities to High-Cost Appraisal and/or Failure Areas

Setting up a correlation between prevention and failure costs is a powerful aid to management of improvement activities. Most organizations do have prevention activities, even if they are spread across departments that perform many actions. Without a quality cost system, however, prevention activities are often spread evenly, and may not exist anywhere in sufficient scope to be effective. As with the appraisal category, alignment may mean increasing, decreasing, or simply reallocating prevention activities.

Key finding: Allocation decisions for prevention efforts need to be based on linkages to current internal and external failure costs, not to appraisal costs.

FOCUS ON THE POSITIVE

Quality management often has a negative connotation. Product quality is seen as a good thing, but the management of quality too often focuses on where it is not: on the mistakes, not on the successes. In the same vein, views of quality costs within your organization may focus on negative issues. Some department managers view quality costs as a measure of their department's mistakes.

To counter this view, focus on the positive aspects of quality cost measurement. By helping to reduce overall organizational costs, a department not only makes the organization more successful, it may also save jobs and therefore retain talent.

But to do this, departments must work together. A manager responsible for order writing would be held responsible for the quality of the orders prepared by their department. The quality of these orders might be dependent on data from the sales force about the floor plans of the customers' many locations. Wrong floor plan data would create wrong orders. Since he or she lacks resources or authority to improve the floor plan data, the order writing department manager could make no improvement in order writing quality. If the sales area is not measured on floor plan accuracy, there would be no improvement in the floor plan data. Setting up a cost of quality measure that follows the entire information stream and then holding all the department managers jointly responsible for improving the overall measure would change the situation entirely.

By focusing on the benefits of cost of quality methods, managers are much more likely to participate and commit themselves to improve management of the *entire business system*. This is where normal cost accounting systems fail to show cross-organizational problems or to highlight effective solutions.

Simplicity and practicality are paramount. Common sense is needed to sort out what costs are significant and which are not. Significance may not mean large. For example, a relatively small measured cost may reflect a larger cost, but the larger cost may not be measurable under the organization's operating constraints. In this case, the smaller cost will have to stand in for the larger one.

In keeping with Juran's previous characterization of quality costs as "gold in the mine," another analogy is useful. Quality costs can be an early warning system. Before there were methane detectors, miners took canaries into underground mine shafts with them. The canaries would pass out from methane concentrations before the gas built up to explosive levels and thus they acted as an early warning device. Quality cost measures often prove more sensitive to product cost or product delivery issues than traditional operational measures, which may hide the real cost of errors and the reasons they occur. They are also "preventive" in that if their warnings are heeded and effective responses are taken, potential losses can be avoided or at least minimized.

2

The Importance of Organizational Environment and Human Psychology in Change

TYPES OF ORGANIZATIONS

There are various ways to categorize organization structures, whether they are manufacturing or service (See Figure 2.1). Such classifications merely identify broad characteristics. And while no organization is at either extreme of these classifications, by looking at the extremes we can identify how organizational differences can impact implementation of a quality cost program.

Organizations, their internal processes, and even their markets, have a lifecycle. And, by necessity, they evolve. Different types of organizations have different needs at different points in their life span. Some organizations age and die, others gain new life or are reorganized into a new

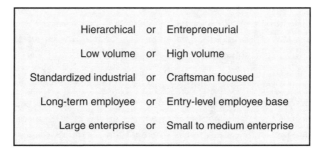

Hierarchical	or	Entrepreneurial
Low volume	or	High volume
Standardized industrial	or	Craftsman focused
Long-term employee	or	Entry-level employee base
Large enterprise	or	Small to medium enterprise

Figure 2.1 Organization classifications.

existence. At any given time, a firm may be in the process of moving from one classification to another. Since all organizations are unique, understanding the current classification can be important to a successful implementation of quality costs, or indeed, any transformative improvement approach.

Hierarchical or Entrepreneurial

In a highly hierarchical environment, most decisions flow from the top downward. Ideas may start anywhere in the organization, but only those driven from above will gain acceptance. Rules are closely obeyed in such organizations, as there are often penalties for employees who are perceived as noncompliant. In such an environment, quality costs may be viewed by lower-level employees as upper management looking for mistakes so punishment can be administered.

In such an atmosphere implementation of any improvement program, including quality cost methods, will be resisted, if not undermined. Several things need to take place before a successful quality costs program can be deployed:

- First, find several major cost issues as examples

- Second, find the root causes for these issues

- Third, fix these issues while avoiding blame

- Fourth, publicize the issues and their solutions so that employees can see that quality costs are being used to root out systemic problems, not as a means of punishment

Management must dispel the idea that quality cost analysis is a just the latest program *du jour* to control and punish employees. In the quality cost method, workers are not the issue—processes are. Often, quality costs can be traced to policies or practices that were needed at one time to address a specific issue. They became part of processes but now either cause more problems than they solve or are simply outdated in the current state of the business and marketplace. Put another way, these costs are not caused by mistakes but by past choices by management.

Strongly hierarchical organizations may form in the absence of strong competition, where customer losses are rare and the marketplace has shown few challenges. If this situation is present, some kind of driver is needed as a motivator. This kind of motivation is called a *burning platform,* and it describes a way of forcing a change in the status quo.

A highly entrepreneurial organization is likely to have an easier time of implementing a quality cost program. Entrepreneurial organizations are driven by innovation and risk, and are by their nature open to change. This is a fertile environment in which to deploy quality cost methods. That is not to say that implementing in this type of organization will be without challenges. Entrepreneurial organizations often have an environment of intense competition between divisions or departments. If one division sees quality costing as their idea, others may reject the concept. To avoid this, management must ensure that one division does not take the idea of quality cost measurement as their own. This problem can be avoided if there is an established method to share best practices. There is nothing inherently wrong in cost reduction competition but it tends to be more successful in a learning organization.

Low Volume or High Volume

Production requirements can affect the implementation success of both improvement efforts and quality costs. Take for example a high-volume bread bakery compared to a low-volume aircraft manufacturer. In the bakery, an approach that gradually reduces process issues and solves quality cost problems will result in a good return over an extended period of time. In such a high-volume business there are plenty of opportunities to try different approaches and gradually change the organization's processes. An aircraft manufacturer, on the other hand, can't take the same approach. Since only relatively few aircraft are produced, and those that are produced must work the first time and be produced without driving up costs, the quality cost drivers for the processes need to be identified early and solutions applied immediately or there could be a severe negative impact on current and future business.

In the high-volume business, a quality cost program can start through trial and error and take a longer time to become institutionalized. In the low-volume business, the program must be planned to succeed right from the start. Success for the low-volume manufacturer depends on close coordination of multiple teams, so early training in quality cost principles is essential to ensure cross-communication at implementation and throughout the relatively short production cycle.

For a service organization, low or high volume issues are different in the core or primary business, as the point of customer contact is usually made on a one-to-one, employee-to-customer basis. For a larger service business, there are back offices or service areas where the high-volume production issues listed above will still apply. The direct-to-customer areas will more often exhibit a low-volume characteristic.

Standardized Industrial or Craftsman Focused

Some organizations operate within an industrial matrix, others in a craftsman environment. For example, companies in the northeast United States often hire employees from a population that has a tradition of being industrial-focused. In such a culture, most employees understand how work is broken down into many small steps, where the steps are performed by separate employees and the smooth functioning of the company depends on all the tasks working together. Therefore, there is easier acceptance of standardized work across the organization regardless of location. In this type of environment, parallel operations in different locations can share the same quality cost matrix and methods for solving cost issues.

Other organizations thrive on a culture of individual skills and contributions. Often located in an agricultural region (or former agricultural region), these organizations prize innovation and individual creativity. As a result, teams work differently. It may be perfectly permissible for two parallel groups doing the same work to have two different operations. In this environment, flexibility is prized and standardization may be seen as an attack on originality and creativity. Therefore, comparison of quality costs and common solutions between seemingly similar divisions can be difficult or impossible in these circumstances. Each division will need to focus on their own performance over time.

High-Turnover/Low-Skill or Low-Turnover/High-Skill Employee Base

Many service enterprises or retail enterprises (such as fast-food franchises or large discount retailers) face the endless task of training new employees only to see them leave for other opportunities. This environment is likely to impact the prevention activities of a quality cost program. Many prevention activities assume that people who are trained in a technique to avoid a problem will simply avoid the problem. The prevention team creates training, employees are trained, and the failure costs shrink. However, if the primary employee base turns over quickly and new recruits arrive with little training, methods of prevention through training may not be as effective. Other approaches are needed. One approach may be to design the work so that mistakes are difficult to make (error prevention) while doing the task.

If most of your employees are long-term and well trained, there can be a different problem. These employees may not see any need to change. If problems found outside a given department or division suggest that a change is needed internally, employees inside the department may not make the connection. They may also develop "tunnel vision" because they simply have not been exposed to any other way to do the processes. To counteract this, management should provide broader training in the overall multi-department system (showing the organization as a linked system of processes) so that all employees understand how their area's work fits into the larger scope of the business. If possible, employees can be temporarily assigned to an upstream process job area. By knowing how the products of their supplier department are used, they can see firsthand the need for process improvement. Employees can also make trips to other organizations for benchmarking purposes.

These two extremes, like the other extremes in this chapter, do not illustrate any particular organization. Your organization may have some of these elements or all of these elements at different locations. What is important is to recognize that quality costs can't be rolled out in every organization in the same manner without consideration of the organizational environment. The examples discussed here illustrate some of the situations to consider in your particular environment.

Large Enterprise or Small to Medium Enterprise

Small to medium enterprises have slightly different quality costs than large enterprises. In both organizations quality costs do not appear to vary in total, but failure costs collect in different areas. For small to medium enterprises, failure costs are proportionally larger in the internal failure category. For larger enterprises, external failure costs are larger. A solution that reduces internal failure costs is not as likely to have the same impact on a larger organization when compared to a small to medium enterprise.

In a doctoral dissertation "Quality Costs and Enterprise Size in the Manufacturing Industry" Suhansa Rodchua found that while failure costs were on average about 70 to 80 percent of total quality costs, small to medium enterprises had a high percentage of internal failure costs and large organizations had a high percentage of external failure costs. See Table 2.1.

In this study, small to medium enterprises were companies with less than 500 employees. The study involved 63 firms.

While the other quality cost categories, prevention and appraisal, did not show significant differences between small to medium enterprises and

Table 2.1   Internal failure costs and external failure costs compared between small to medium enterprises and large enterprises.

	Small to medium enterprises	Large enterprises
Internal failure costs Percent of manufacturing expenses	4.4%	3.1%
External failure costs Percent of manufacturing expenses	2.0%	3.4%

Source: S. Rodchua, "Quality Costs and Manufacturing Size in the Manufacturing Industry: A Survey Research" (unpublished doctoral dissertation) (Indiana State University, 2005).

large firms in Rodchua's study, the differences for failure costs indicate where failure costs appear. Since a larger portion of failure costs for small to medium enterprises appears before shipment, small to medium firms need to focus on internal failures before trying to capture and analyze their external failure costs. Larger firms would be best served to apply equal efforts to internal and external failure cost reduction.[1] (Contact Dr. Rodchua, School of Technology, University of Central Missouri, Warrensburg, Missouri.)

THE BALANCE BETWEEN ORGANIZATIONAL CHANGE AND YEAR-TO-YEAR CONSISTENCY

A quality cost reporting system requires long-term thinking. Each year brings new quality costs into focus and new ways of measuring what were previously unmeasured costs. This will cause a reporting dilemma—do you change the reports to cover the new costs or do you keep reports the same to allow for year-to-year comparisons?

Adding the new costs during breaks between measurement periods (year or quarter) usually makes the most sense. At the same time, keeping the detailed cost categories separate in old files will make backward recalculations possible. In this way, a multiyear comparison can be made even after the new cost report is initiated. Some costs may not belong in the new report but measuring them for a short time after they have been removed will help maintain consistency in making multiyear comparisons.

THE WHY OF CHANGE

"Why?" is usually our first thought about change.

Why should we change? Why disrupt our lives? Why cause more work? Change makes us uncomfortable in the present and uncertain about the future. If it ain't broke, don't fix it. Leave well enough alone. It may be a good idea, but . . . let me tell you why it won't work. We could try that, but . . . here are all the problems you'll have. I'm all for change, but . . . don't change too fast. Our business is different. This is the way we've always done it.

So it goes, in all types of organizations and even in our personal lives.

The "why" and "but" adherents have good reasons for their concerns. Experience tells them that change is indeed risky—that failure is an option. Doing something different could put in jeopardy a fragile set of processes. It could be expensive. It could absorb needed resources. It might expose our vulnerability and embarrass us.

There is a fortune cookie message that says, "You learn more by falling than by the fear of falling." This is the most fundamental element of organizational and personal improvement. Deming's plan–do–study–act cycle tells us to continuously try something new, learn from it, and try again and again—each time applying what we learn to become better.

Michael Jordan once said, "I missed more than 9000 shots in my career. I lost almost 300 games. On 26 occasions I was entrusted to take the game-winning shot . . . and missed. And I have failed over and over and over again in my life. And that is why . . . I succeed."[2]

Life teaches us that, no matter how much we wish we could, we can't avoid risk—there is greater risk in doing nothing than trying something different. Those people and organizations who succeed and become great aren't afraid of risk—aren't afraid of trying new things, aren't afraid of falling down and getting back up again. To do otherwise means we remain still while others pass us—others will do well while we decline.

Change is the most fundamental element of human life and organizations. Change fuels the engine of performance excellence. Yet, the result of a four-year study by LeadershipIQ showed that the major reason American CEOs get fired is failure to sell and manage needed organizational change.

APPROACHES TO ORGANIZATIONAL CHANGE

There are some elements common to making organizational change work in any organization. These are just a few approaches. There are many others.

Situation: It is human nature to resist change. Change isn't easy for most of us. Even if we are in a field that promotes change, we ourselves can recoil from it. The concept of comfort zones helps to explain some of our inherent resistance to change. A comfort zone is a mental image of where an individual thinks they fit. It can create barriers to where an individual needs to go even as it reduces their stress. This is true of groups as well. One illuminating example is that of the Swiss watchmakers. For centuries they were the center of the watchmaking trade. They saw watches as solely a mechanical device, with gears and other moving parts. When digital watches reached the world market Swiss watchmakers held fast to their paradigm. The result was disastrous for the Swiss watch industry—significantly reduced market share and job losses. The same is happening today in other industries.

Approach: The only permanent thing in life is change. To help mitigate the natural tendency to resist change, help employees understand a change they have already experienced and explain how future change can be weathered like the change they already managed. Understanding what the future will look like, and our position in it, makes change easier. Do this exercise yourself: imagine how your prior self, from five or 10 years ago, would react to being placed in your current job with no additional training. For most of us, total bewilderment would occur. New software, new communications, altered functions and relationships, all would be hurdles. Now think of yourself today; you managed the changes, and you can do your job well. You learned, you coped, you changed.

Situation: In a sense, all employees are responsible for minimizing risk in their organization by finding and fixing problems. Unfortunately, there is a human tendency to deny that a problem or risk exists. Some of us tend to do this not overtly but below the level of conscious thought. Others deny problems through a natural defensive mechanism. We don't want to be seen as creating problems or perpetuating them. If we are part of a problem will we lose our job? Will we be reprimanded? What are the consequences? Will there be punishment?

Approach: We can't reduce risk and business problems by denying they exist. And punishing employees for working in broken processes won't improve an organization. Management must build trust so employees are constantly working to find problems and improve business processes. As soon as employees understand that management recognizes and compensates for organizational improvement, they will make that a core part of their job.

Situation: Another element of resistance to change is similar to psychological projection. In psychological projection an individual projects their own thoughts, feelings, or bias onto another person, and infers that others are feeling or thinking what they are feeling or thinking.

In an operational environment, we often shift problems to others. When asked to change an operational method an employee may say, "I could do that but so-and-so over there can't, (or won't) do it." When you talk to the other employee, they respond the same way. Each is projecting the problem onto others around them because they resist changing from a comfortable to a new and uncomfortable environment.

Approach: Change is often easier if you get the work group to meet together and talk about the change. In a group, if everyone accepts the idea for a temporary trial period, everyone tends to go along. After the trial period, get the group together and discuss the change. If the change worked, then implementing it on a permanent basis should become easier. On the other hand, if the attempt failed, find out why. With the group, brainstorm possible improvements that would allow the new process to work. Following this, try the change again with the necessary alterations in place.

FORMING, STORMING, NORMING, PERFORMING

For change to occur, it often takes a range of involved individuals. Most organizations use a team approach to help create involvement and buy-in for the desired changes. A properly constituted team will help the change implementation fit the organization and tailor the changes to the diverse areas of the organization.

To have effective teams, it helps to follow a proven methodology. The team development process published by Bruce Tuckman in 1965 may help with these approaches. In summary, Tuckman's process looks like this:

Stage 1   *Forming.* Team members disagree, and roles are unclear. The team leader directs while members test the system and the leader.

Stage 2 *Storming*. Team members form factions, and roles are in dispute as the purpose becomes clearer. The leader coaches while members keep focus on the project and make compromises.

Stage 3 *Norming*. The team creates a consensus, and rules are understood. The leader facilitates and enables while members show some leadership themselves and build unity.

Stage 4 *Performing*. The team connects with overall strategy and operates with autonomy. The leader delegates tasks and projects while the members look after each other.[3]

Change isn't easy because people and organizations are complex. But continuous improvement is necessary to survive. When all else fails, it can simply be about getting the right people on the bus. Effective teamwork is all about having the right people focused in the right way on the right things.

3

Overview of Constructing a Cost of Quality Measure

HOW OFTEN TO REPORT—TIME PERIOD CONSIDERATIONS

Cost of quality reports can be issued annually, semiannually, quarterly, monthly, weekly, or daily. Before you begin, decide how often you need to publish the reports. Some things to consider are:

- What is the reason for measuring? How will the report be used and/or responded to?

- Would multiple frequencies be useful? You may issue a high-level report quarterly, with more detailed reports issued monthly to lower-level managers.

- Your organization may have a normal reporting period fixed by management meeting dates.

- Publishing reports too often may consume unnecessary resources—publishing too infrequently will destroy any sense of urgency and stall improvement progress.

- How is your organization used to seeing time period comparisons? Current year-to-date versus previous year-to-date? This month versus this year to date? Last 12 months versus previous year-end? Your reports should mirror other management reports so that the cost of quality report is viewed as part of the overall reporting and measurement system and not an add-on.

There are normally three data time frames in most reports—current information, some type of basis for comparison, and past performance. An effective trend review needs a clear downward or upward slope, and this often takes more than 12 data points.

For current information, there are several approaches:

• *Quarterly.* This level is recommended by FDA and ISO guidelines as a minimum. While this will reduce the resources used to create the report, data will have to be summarized over the three months. Progress will be slowed, as managers will not see results often enough. If an issue arises, reporting of the results will occur late and key people involved may not remember what caused the problem. This timing should be reserved for senior leaders or for early stages of implementation of a quality costs system.

• *Monthly.* Monthly reports are more timely, hold report creation resources down, and are close enough to cost events and problems so that employees can associate measurements with operational issues.

• *Weekly.* Weekly reports are useful for operational defect counts and other quality cost drivers. This kind of reporting is good for fast-paced organizations. Care needs to be exercised not to overreact to single-week fluctuations; use a physical graph so that everyone can see the overall performance trend. This will also help identify common cause variation. It is much easier to make corrections when the issues are less than a week old, but multiweek reports may show important trends that demand different action than one might take for an immediate operational fix. One problem with this speed of reporting is the slower reaction of legacy data systems. If your old data system takes several weeks to assess the final and complete situation, this speed of reporting may result in managerial frustration.

For time-based comparison information, there are several approaches:

• *Goals (established and updated periodically).* For managers thinking of future situations, setting a goal is important. Setting goals for quality costs has many aspects in common with setting budgetary goals. Regular review of goals and status measurements is critical to task completion.

• *Stretch goals.* Stretch goals create a sense of urgency and help an organization leapfrog to accomplish objectives that may have otherwise been considered impossible. Stretch goals require management support and an environment of trust where failing, learning, and retrying is the accepted business practice. In a supportive environment, stretch goals create a cooperative dialog of "how can we do this?" But stretch goals can also create panic, disillusionment, or negative behavior if employees feel it is impossible to accomplish the objectives and management may react in a negative way to initial failures.

• *Year to date.* By adding up the results from the beginning of a calendar year to the present, a historical total can be produced. This total allows judgment of current information against recent history. One potential problem with this approach is that data early in the year may fluctuate, and data late in the year may be too static. As a result, comparisons may not be useful and yearly totals may not reflect progress. Year-to-date reports can be a good indicator only if the data are scrutinized for fluctuations and trends.

• *Last* X *(number of months, weeks, days).* As a running period report, this can provide the same benefit as a year-to-date measure but it avoids the problem of changes during the year. Remember to factor in your organization's product lifecycle; if your product mix is seasonal, show several cycles. Of course, you can include several of these historical measures to allow a clear picture for your managers.

Both goals and historical reference time periods are sometimes used along with current information to allow a past, present, and future comparison.

LEADING AND LAGGING COSTS

Thought should be given to process time delay, providing the significant benefit of linking cause and effect (or prevention and failure). For example, if warranty costs are significant and prevention costs linked to warranty issues occur 12 months prior to the warranty costs, a means of leading or lagging these costs will allow them to align. This will highlight the cause-and-effect relationship.

These considerations should guide your choices of sources of data. Keeping accurate historical comparisons will become important as the report is used to drive change. *Before the search for data begins is the time to think through reporting period needs.* Remember to keep the general approach similar to other reports used in your organization. This will promote understanding and acceptance.

SINGLE LAYER OR MULTILAYER REPORTING

If your organization is large, there may be several operational areas that need different amounts of detail in their own cost of quality reports. This issue can influence source choices, report timing, assembly methods, and goal setting.

Such multilayer or multilevel reports may be created by different individuals, which can impact consistency and data integrity. To avoid confusion, always use the same data sources for common information. Set up a coordinated schedule for the various levels of reports, and leave time to work out discrepancies between areas during the reporting cycle.

The best approach is to have a single source for reporting. This may be hard to manage as it is common for managers to want to see their own data in just a little different format than someone else. Operational managers may insist on doing some manual tweaking of their own. If standard sources of data and standard reporting formats are not used, reconciliation of higher-level management reports may be made difficult.

WHAT YOU NEED TO KNOW

As a leader, knowledge that you need as you develop and implement your quality cost program can be divided into three major areas:

1. Quality cost principles

2. Specific techniques for implementing quality costs

3. Your company, its key drivers, and interrelationships

The first two (quality cost principles and specific techniques) you can obtain in this book. For those who wish more information on areas 1 and 2 above, there are additional resources in the bibliography.

Quality Cost Principles

At a minimum, you will need to know what quality costs are and how they are defined. Having deeper knowledge so that you can interpret these principles in the context of your organization will enhance your chances for success. The principles include the definitions of quality cost categories—*prevention, appraisal, internal failure,* and *external failure.*

The elements within the categories will vary in their application at different organizations. Keep Appendix A handy for reference as you implement your program. As you work on the implementation, you will find your depth of understanding increasing on those elements that apply to your organization.

WHAT OTHERS NEED TO KNOW

Teams

To implement quality costs in any size organization you will need some type of team. For larger organizations with multiple divisions or work units, you need more than one team. The team's objectives should include defining the costs of quality in your organization, determining how to measure them, and deciding what will be done with the results.

To set up a successful team, consider the following questions and your organization's type:

- *Who should be on the team?* Who knows about the systems? Who knows management concerns? Who has critical thinking skills? Who has creative thinking skills? Some team members will be needed at the beginning and some may be needed only at the end.

- *What constitutes good teamwork?* What do you expect from the team members? How will you know when the team has accomplished its objective?

- *Who should be the team leader?* You may not be the best choice for leader. Consider the team objectives and who may be the best one to keep the team focused.

- *When should the team be cross-functional?* This will vary depending on the areas within your organization. If the quality costs are primarily from multiple departments, a cross-functional team involving those departments is necessary.

- *Should membership be voluntary?* Voluntary membership is best. But there may be critical individuals who should to be encouraged to participate because of their operational knowledge.

Individuals in various roles and levels within your organization will have different needs, and the size of your organization will affect the level of understanding required.

Accounting

Involvement of the accounting or controller's department can be critical. Ideally, they should be partners, driving the portion of the effort related to cost system understanding and references to profit and loss statements and helping with obtaining accurate cost information from your organization's chart of accounts. If they are either not involved or only superficially involved, your program may be seen as just another quality project. This will severely limit your chances for success. Some organizations consider quality projects to be limited to the quality assurance department. If this is true at your organization, you might avoid using the word "quality" altogether.

Management accounting should be represented on the quality cost assessment team, be a source of data, and lend credibility to the reporting. They can remove communication barriers as they can relate the effort to implement a quality cost program directly to the profit and loss statements. Bear in mind that the organization will certainly see cost of quality reporting as extra work.

Training

Providing training in quality cost principles is a central part of making your program a reality. While quality cost concepts have been around a long time, and you may be familiar with them, you need to be sure the other key players in your organization know enough to apply the general concepts to your situation.

The American Society for Quality periodically offers a course on cost of quality methods. Check their Web site, www.asq.org, for training and certification, under the topic Quality Management.

Part II

Application Notes

4

Tactics in Building Cost of Quality Measures

If you are an executive looking for an overview, you can stop here. What follows is information about implementation and there may be more detail than you need.

On the other hand, you may be interested in some of this detail or you may be charged with the implementation itself. Chapters 4 through 6 will be helpful if this is the case.

If you are only looking for an overview, you may provide this book to others in your organization charged with implementation. This will help them gain an understanding of both basic concepts and implementation details.

SEEKING SYSTEM GURUS, INTERNAL AND EXTERNAL

Since you will be using data from your organization's systems, seeking out those in your organization who understand the intricate (or perhaps just unobserved) aspects of your internal systems will help you when questions come up such as, "Did we include all the significant costs?"

It's likely that there is someone in your organization who understands the way your costing systems work. Chances are, this person works in the accounting area of your company. This is a key reason why the active participation of your accounting or controller's department is critical to your success in measuring and implementing a cost of quality approach.

If you are at a small subsidiary or plant where no one has this knowledge, there may be documentation of the accounting systems.

Older employees may be the most useful. Long-time, experienced staff can provide the rationale for the way your organization's measurement systems were constructed and the key to understanding how they work now.

There may also be newly hired individuals at your organization that have been exposed to cost of quality in another company. The outside perspective these people have may help you better understand your organization's accounting and measurement systems.

THE KISS PRINCIPLE

The acronym "KISS" stands for "Keep it simple, stupid." The point is, don't make a task more complicated than it needs to be. Convoluted and complicated processes lose your audience, tend to cost more, and frustrate participants.

One way to keep a cost of quality analysis uncomplicated is to always choose the simplest way to collect information and then be willing to change your approach if it doesn't work. The simplest processes and measurements often prove to be not only good enough but substantially more robust than more elaborate approaches. Your method of cost of quality measurements must be easily understood so corrective action appears obvious. Even capturing approximately 80 percent or more of the costs is often sufficient. It is important to not get "analysis paralysis." The intent is to focus on the highest loss contributors. By following the Pareto approach to cost indicators and addressing the top two or three, significant gains will be made.

For smaller organizations, an initial focus on failure costs may be preferred. See case study #2 on CRC Industries in Appendix B.

Start by building a simple spreadsheet in which to enter the data. Spreadsheets have the advantage of being easily understood by most employees. After a spreadsheet is used and the relationships between the data and the impact on operations are understood, then a database can be built using the simplest possible architecture. If your organization doesn't have sophisticated data warehouses, Microsoft Access is easy to use and all the prior work in spreadsheets can be imported into it.

REPURPOSING EXISTING PROCESSES

One way to simplify is to use existing costing reports or systems. While it is doubtful that a cost of quality system will be able to be built using only totals or subtotals from existing costing systems, there will be some existing reports that will provide a good fit. An example might be a cost report that shows product returns from the field; another example would be a report that summarizes accounting credits provided to customers for unsold merchandise. If these credits or expenses are not recovered later, there would be little need to dig into this report for details; the total value from the current report would be satisfactory. Don't reinvent something that works well.

There may be existing systems that track instances of quality problems. For example, an organization has a report that keeps track of the number of customer complaints. While this may not be a cost report, all you need to convert this information into a cost of quality source is to place a cost on the number of instances from the report. An engineering study could easily estimate the cost of an average complaint. Perhaps different types of complaints will have significantly different costs. If so, these should be quantified in the original report. Backed by a sound engineering study, there should be little dispute that a count of customer complaints multiplied by their average cost would represent, in aggregate, the cost of customer complaints. See Table 4.1.

Often, an existing department budget may provide all you need. For example, a manufacturing plant may total all the inspectors' expenses under one budget. This is an element of the appraisal costs category. In this case, you need to determine if the entire budget is devoted to inspection; if there are significant non-inspection costs in this budget (such as a quality engineer who sets up systems and trains new inspectors) you may need to make some form of adjustment to the budget costs you collect from the accounting system. Similarly, if there are costs associated with plant inspections that do not appear in this budget area, you may need to collect them and add them in. An example might be testing by an outside laboratory. Testing expenses are usually part of appraisal, but these costs in your organization may currently be totaled in a general account for purchased outside services. See Figure 4.1.

Table 4.1 Event counts and cost per event.

Complaint type	Monthly complaints	Average cost per complaint	Monthly complaint cost
Serious—A level	4	$1500	4 × 1500 = $6,000
Normal—B level	65	$94	65 × 94 = $6,110
Total monthly cost			$12,110

Inspection department monthly expenses (from accounting records):

Jan	Feb	Mar	Apr	May
$101,456	$95,003	$86,051	$123,443	$55,010

Less engineer expenses (estimated from average salary):

$2,055	$2,055	$2,055	$2,055	$2,055

Plus outside testing lab expenses (from invoices):

$500	$1,506	$0	$150	$56

= total appraisal expenses:

Jan	Feb	Mar	Apr	May
$99,901	$94,454	$83,996	$121,538	$53,011

Figure 4.1   Modifying existing accounting results.

Table 4.2   Labor reporting database table—original.

Week date	Employee	Hours	Labor rate	(Empty)
12/10/07	#2754	40	$56	
12/17/07	#2754	40	$56	
12/10/07	#113	40	$35	
12/17/07	#113	40	$35	

If you have a database at your company that tracks business data and you have a need to subdivide some costs at a transaction level, you might need to add classification data to the records in the database. While adding a new field to an IT systems database can be an expensive proposition, there may be some unused text fields in the database. By repurposing these fields to identify cost of quality data, you can make an inexpensive change to the database that allows sorting of quality costs.

The following example shows how this might work. The original data table (Table 4.2) has time records for two employees over two weeks. The two employees are paid different wage rates. There is an unused column in the data table.

By adding a column to classify the labor hours into several categories, and splitting the time into the three categories, the table looks like Table 4.3.

Now the costs can be easily summarized into the three categories (see Figure 4.2). The third category, Other, is not really useful at this stage.

Table 4.3   Labor reporting database table—modified.

Week date	Employee	Hours	Labor rate	Work class	Quality cost category
12/10/07	#2754	37	$56	A	A = Appraisal
12/10/07	#2754	3	$56	P	P = Prevention
12/17/07	#2754	15	$56	A	O = Other
12/17/07	#2754	20	$56	O	
12/17/07	#2754	5	$56	P	
12/10/07	#113	40	$35	O	
12/17/07	#113	35	$35	O	
12/17/07	#113	5	$35	A	

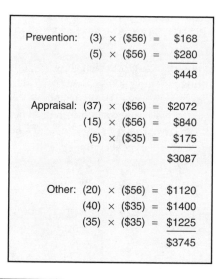

Figure 4.2   Summary of results of adding an index field to an existing database.

NEW DATA COLLECTION SYSTEMS

Setting up a new data collection system is a difficult and expensive task. If your organization is in need of a major change, then it may be a good opportunity. Otherwise, justifying and estimating the cost of a new IT system can eat up all your available time and offer only a limited return.

A better option is to add new space to an existing database or system, if one exists that can be customized. If you start with a full understanding of an existing IT system and you think through what you really need to track quality costs, you might need to make only a small addition to a current application.

As mentioned above, you can build a small local database using software such as Microsoft Access, but you need to be wary of the long-term costs of creating a small stand-alone system. How will it stay current? Who will understand it and maintain it as your personnel changes and your cost of quality approaches change? Can you build it without creating a separate, but parallel, data source? Keeping the data clean will become a difficult task if you have multiple entries of the same information. Talk to your IT staff to make sure your own stand-alone system is a good choice.

SOURCES AND METHODS OF DATA TRANSFER OR COLLECTION

Starting with the end product, a report that shows quality costs and goals, you can work backward to identify sources. Just behind the report you need summary data, and probably more detailed tables behind that. At some point, your data sources will split into different types of transmission or collection. Table 4.4 shows a list of methods for collecting data for a report—from the simplest to the most complex.

Verbal Information

This may be the worst approach. With this approach, it is not possible to double-check the source data.

Written Paper Notes

A step above verbal communication. While this does allow checking, filing and searching paper notes has many drawbacks. The notes need to have the date and time the information was collected or processed and, ideally, the name of the person who provided the data. The need to retype the data adds a source of error.

E-mails with Embedded Text or Data

A step more advanced than paper notes, e-mails have the advantage of being searchable. There is an automatic trail from whoever sent the data,

Table 4.4 Pros and cons for methods of data collection.

Method	Pro	Con	Notes
Verbal information	Fast	No record	Not recommended
Written paper notes	Fast	Unsearchable	Not recommended
E-mails with embedded text or data	Fast, recorded source, searchable	Mutable format	Not for large amount of data
E-mails with attached spreadsheets	Recorded source, flexible, error limited	Must coordinate structures	Five to 60 values
Spreadsheets shared over a network	Instant update	Broken links, network issues	
Database storage	Single source	Complex to make	Good for major implementations
Full data automation	Standardized	Inflexible, expensive	Not recommended for changing organizations

and simple text can be copied and pasted from an e-mail to a spreadsheet for reporting purposes, avoiding retyping errors. The drawbacks include a changing structure each time the e-mail is created and potential problems if the data are pasted into the e-mail as an image instead of simple text. Images in e-mails can not be used in a spreadsheet via a copy-and-paste technique. This type of e-mail data needs to be retyped, so it also poses a risk for error.

This approach works well only when a few values are needed from a particular source for each report cycle.

E-mails with Attached Spreadsheets

If there are more than a few values to retype, the opportunity for error in transcription becomes more significant. When there are between five to 60 values transmitted each report period, you may choose to use the copy and paste function to take them from the e-mailed document and move the data into your spreadsheet. In this case, the sender should be using a spreadsheet to send you the data. The values must be placed in a consistent location in the sender's spreadsheet or you will be required to alter your spreadsheet each time you paste.

Setting up spreadsheets with external links to other spreadsheets is not a good idea. There are too many ways to break the links and most data that belong together will fit on one spreadsheet. The data may be in different tabs within a spreadsheet; external links are connections to truly separate spreadsheets with different file names.

Spreadsheets Shared over a Network

In this approach, one department makes up a spreadsheet and the receiving department creates a link from one spreadsheet to the previous one, across a local computer network. Updates of data are passed as the received spreadsheet is opened.

There are many difficulties with this approach. First, the network links must remain sound. This is not always a guarantee. Second, there needs to be some kind of message from one area to the next that the periodically changing data has been updated. If a problem is found, there should be a way to alert those downstream that a new version has been set up to they can open and update their spreadsheet.

Database Storage with Common or Custom Extracts

Using a database to store your information is a good approach. Using a query from the database, you can limit the data, collect it, and summarize it to the needed level all with one predefined action. That way the data will be consistent from time to time and area to area. If the data changes more often than your report frequency, you will need to coordinate the timing of the extracts; otherwise, different people querying the database at different times will get different values. This will create confusion for the users of your report.

Databases provide phenomenal access to data. They are fast and help to keep everyone looking at the same data. They also allow rapid drill-down into deeper layers of detail. For example, you may have a quality cost report that shows that a plant is not making their goal. The first question will be, "why?" You may need to drill down into areas of (perhaps) unreported details to see which department(s) is/are lagging. Other data will be needed as you drill down. Volume of products or services, types of product or services, and so on, will be needed to understand the causes of the discrepancy. Having predefined queries that show these details will help when the inevitable "why" question surfaces.

While there is merit in streamlining reports and reducing the volume of data handled, today's high-speed data handling systems allow extra data to be kept without a major increase in resources. As information technology continues to advance, cost of storage space will continue to fall. As time passes, there will be situations where the additional data is found useful. As an example, there may be a department that only occasionally affects costs of quality but does so in a major way when it occurs. Tracking the expenses of this department can help expedite the report generation process.

Changes in loss reporting systems or major reorganizations often create a need to track data from multiple sources. Even if this year's report does not use a source that the previous year's report used, keeping the old source will be helpful when multiyear comparisons are needed.

The appropriate level of detail is dependent on the level of reporting desired. For example, if the cost of quality report covers several plants, and no department detail is reported below the plant level, then no department-level detail is required in the database extract. The database may possess department-level data, but handling this detail in the copy and paste transfer to your report spreadsheet will make troubleshooting difficult, as well as forcing a summarization process in the spreadsheet that can result in a slow calculation speed.

Databases that lack a copy and paste output option should be avoided. These antiquated applications place a severe restriction on data reporting flexibility since all reporting must be done via their limited report-making tools, and combining one database's information with another's information requires either a manual retyping step or some kind of background data link that must be programmed by an IT expert.

Databases may be costly to build if you have an older system or multiple systems that do not share data transfer options. In this case, making a database is not a first step; rather, it is a step that you may take if your first cost of quality reports show value to the organization and the use of the data can help other projects in areas like inventory control or material control. With a broader area of business support, you can make a good case for a major database overhaul.

Full Data Automation

This is where a custom programming solution is used. You may create a series of reporting modules that automatically retrieve data and format reports, or you may purchase a package that provides this functionality. While this may work initially, there can be some drawbacks. As your business changes, altering the reporting can prove challenging. If the reporting is from a package, you will need to be sure that the software company can and will keep the package up to date as your operating system changes. Traveling the cost of quality road is usually a long-term approach, so make sure your system will provide you with both flexibility and long-term support.

COMMON SOURCES FOR ASSEMBLING QUALITY COSTS

Let's assume you will use a spreadsheet to assemble the quality costs report. You will probably have many different sources of information for your cost of quality reports and some necessary manipulations to create your report, so using some kind of software will be necessary. Spreadsheets are widely available, simple to use, and powerful enough to do the data manipulations for this type of report. Examples provided here will use Microsoft Excel formats and terms (see Table 4.5).

Table 4.5   Pros and cons of sources of quality cost data.

Source	Pro	Con
Using budget and expense sources	Ties to accounting	Limited details
Additions and subtractions from accounts	Makes quality cost elements show clearly	Needs documentation, periodic review
Head counts and salary amounts	Makes quality cost elements show clearly	Needs documentation, periodic review
Event counts and cost per event	Applies cost to operational measures	Needs detailed study to set up, periodic review
Yield losses	Primary internal failure measure	Must be accurate on average, may not be available
Special credits	Can be large	May be infrequent, needs management awareness and communication
Using expected values	Handles large, rare items	Must have consensus on probabilities
Chargeback systems	Improves perceived fairness	Can overgrow and redirect resources
Manual corrections	Fix inevitable glitches	Can institutionalize workarounds

Using Budget and Expense Sources

The simplest approach to calculating cost of quality is to use budgeting accounts as a source for expense costs. Using budgeted or planned costs is one option, but since budgets are only a plan, it is usually best to use actual expenses in your cost of quality reports.

Starting with your organization's chart of accounts, choose actual expenses from accounts that relate most directly to the elements of cost of quality. Some examples include: quality engineering departments, inspection departments, auditing departments, rework departments, departments that track customer issues, and so on. In many cases these departments will be 100 percent involved in cost of quality work but may not refer to it in those terms. In most cases, just taking the total expenses of these departments and collecting the data into your report is the best approach. In any case, you need to check with the area manager to ensure that there are no significant costs included in these accounts that lie outside the cost of quality measure.

Additions and Subtractions from Accounts

On occasion, some of these selected departments will include major costs that do not apply to the cost of quality. In these cases, you need to make adjustments to the reported expense. The actual amount removed will vary from year to year and from area to area. There may be some expenses that are not included in these accounts that you will need to add to make the report reflect reality. The primary decision to remove or keep these costs in the report depends on the following:

- Will the size of the adjustment materially change decisions based on the quality cost report?

- Will the modification of the source data undermine the credibility of the cost of quality report itself?

An inspection department may have a manager whose salary is not included in that account, but rather is paid out of a higher-level administrative department. Since this manager's expense is directly related to the costs of inspection (that is, without inspections this manager would not be necessary) this cost should be added to the other inspection costs.

For example: A manager for the inspection department is in a pay grade that averages $54,000 per year. This works out to $4,500 per month, so that amount is added to the other appraisal expenses (see Figure 4.3).

Alternatively, there may be costs in one department (such as inspection) that relate to a different category of quality costs (such as prevention).

An inspection department may have rework costs included that are actually part of internal failure costs. Another example is where a quality engineer is tasked with setting up inspection plans and training inspectors on new products. If this engineer's salary is included in the inspection department, then their salary should be placed into the prevention category.

Figure 4.4 shows the total department expense as tracked by the accounting department.

Inspection department monthly expenses (from accounting records):

Jan	Feb	Mar	Apr	May
$101,456	$95,003	$86,051	$123,443	$55,010

Less engineer expenses (estimated from average salary):

$2,055	$2,055	$2,055	$2,055	$2,055

Plus outside testing lab expenses (from invoices):

$500	$1,506	$0	$150	$56

Plus department manager expense:

$4,500	$4,500	$4,500	$4,500	$4,500

= total appraisal expenses:

Jan	Feb	Mar	Apr	May
$104,401	$98,954	$88,496	$126,038	$57,511

Figure 4.3   Adding manager expenses to accounting data.

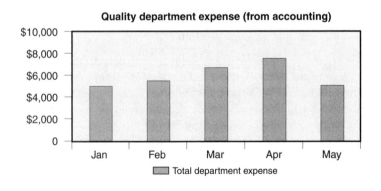

Figure 4.4   Basic department expense accounting data chart.

This amount includes a quality engineer, rework costs, and inspection expense. No manager expense is included, as the quality manager is paid from the plant general budget, not the quality department budget. To turn this into prevention, inspection, and rework categories, several changes need to be made:

- Add the manager expense
- Move the engineer expense to a prevention category
- Move the rework expense to a rework category

Table 4.6 shows the values collected from accounting and records from the quality department.

Figure 4.5 shows the alterations.

Figure 4.6 depicts how the final inspection amount compares to the original total department expense from the accounting department.

Financial databases often contain department-level expenses, but breaking the costs into lower levels can mean applying a fixed percentage to the monthly total. These approaches do not allow for more detailed investigations into monthly peaks or sudden shifts in costs.

For example, small changes in production will probably not change the number of inspectors, and the costs of inspection will tend to remain constant. Large changes, however, such as an added production shift, are likely to mean more inspectors. If inspection is a very large portion of the costs of quality, then tracking the inspectors' time is necessary.

The approach of tracking detailed inspection costs is not a permanent program. It should be implemented on a temporary basis and phased out once process control and prevention activities have reduced the inspection

Table 4.6 Combined quality department data and accounting data.

	Jan	Feb	Mar	Apr	May
Total department expense (before)	$5000	$5500	$6700	$7500	$5100
Manager expense (add)	$4500	$4500	$4500	$4500	$4500
Engineer expense (deduct)	($2055)	($2055)	($2055)	($2055)	($2055)
Rework expense (deduct)	($900)	($1900)	($2560)	($1010)	($950)
Final inspection amount (after)	$6545	$6045	$6585	$8935	$7145

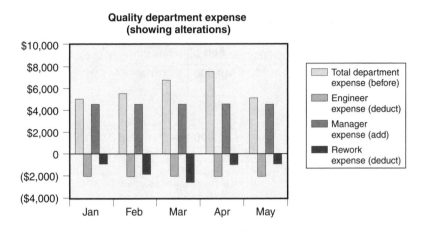

Figure 4.5   Department expense data with alterations chart.

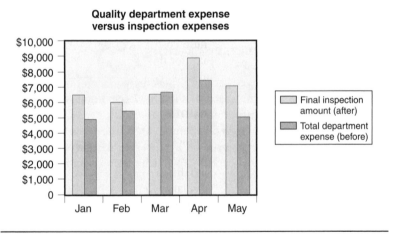

Figure 4.6   Department expenses before and after chart.

workload. So this area of quality costs may be something that increases tracking data, but then reduces it as the situation is improved.

Another situation occurs where a manager estimates that 35 percent of an account's expenses are due to the elements of quality cost. Here, it is easy to collect the entire monthly expense and apply a factor of 35 percent in the spreadsheet. This way, you can modify the percentage after the

Table 4.7 Fractional modification of quality costs.

	Jan	Feb	Mar	Apr	May
Maintenance department expense	$17,500	$19,000	$18,430	$15,657	$19,433
Percentage for calibration	40%	40%	40%	40%	40%
Calibration expense	$7,000	$7,600	$7,372	$6,263	$7,773

periodic review of the nature of cost of quality data sources. This type of modification, like the others listed, needs to be well documented so that new managers can understand the report contents.

In the example shown in Table 4.7, a firm has a department that handles equipment calibration and normal machine maintenance. Over the course of a year, the recalibration effort averages 40 percent of the department's work time.

This splitting and moving of costs will allow you to determine if changes in tasks actually reduce failure costs. Such an impact may show you that prevention costs are too small for the failure costs in the process and support an increase in prevention resource allocation.

Head Counts and Salary Amounts

Estimating the amount of expense to move can be done in several ways. You may use an individual's actual salary, but this may not be accurate over time as different individuals move into different positions. Also, not many people will be pleased if their actual salary is made public. One approach is to take the average salary for the position and use it in the report. That way, no one's actual salary is revealed, and the amount of the salary will reflect a typical cost for that function in your organization. The use of a typical (rather than actual) cost is satisfactory to measure cost of quality changes over time. Obviously, the elimination or addition of positions performing the functions being measured must be reflected in the cost of quality reports. Periodic review of the content of and sources for the cost of quality reporting is a necessity.

If there are several situations where the same position is involved in a particular activity, you can take the number of positions and just multiply them by the average cost, then use this as the cost to move from one account to another.

Event Counts and Cost per Event

There are other types of costs that can be calculated in this manner. Many events occur that can be related to cost of quality: rejections of shipments, corrective actions, trips to suppliers or customers to act on issues, and so on. While the costs for some of these events may vary from situation to situation, calculating an average cost may be useful if the event happens frequently enough.

For example, your shipping department may keep track of back orders. Obtaining the cost for a typical back order is a one-time task. If there are 40 back orders in a month, and the cost per back order is $100, that month has a quality cost of $4000 for back orders. The spreadsheet would need to be updated with number of back orders each month, and the cost per back order would need to be checked should the process or cost of handling back orders change.

Yield Losses

Internal failure costs often fall into three subcategories:

- Cost of production losses

- Inventory corrections

- Rework

Most organizations that produce products have some kind of inventory control system that reports losses. Many have some kind of production yield measurement system. These often track losses during production, hopefully applying a realistic cost to the partially completed parts as they are discarded.

Costs of production losses can vary significantly, depending on where the loss occurs. If production losses are large, beware of systems that simply apply the cost of the raw material to production losses. This will undervalue the cost of yield losses and discourage efforts to reduce them. The undervaluation occurs because the labor that has been spent to bring the parts to a partial stage of completion is not included in the loss cost.

Excess production costs for service industries are more difficult to track, but they can be estimated. For example, some of the labor in a restaurant should track with the number of patrons served. Kitchen hours and cleanup hours would follow the number of meals served, even if wait staff time did not. Paid time spent in these areas in excess of a historical norm could serve as an estimate of quality cost.

Inventory corrections involve some kind of identification of the difference between what the official inventory count says and what is physically present. The ideal is to have no variance, but that usually does not happen. If production uses a part to make a product, but some of the parts are defective and discarded during production and not recorded, the official inventory of parts will be higher than the physical count. At some time, a count of inventory will show this, and a correction will be made to the official inventory record. This correction is a quality cost. See Table 4.8.

Inventory shrinkage is one cost that is present in both manufacturing and service industries, unless the service is one that involves no materials.

Some organizations will have sophisticated systems to track inventory changes. For instance, production workers may have the ability to record the quantity of component parts used along with the number of completed products; a system then calculates the number of parts expected to be used to make the products, subtract it from the worker's recorded parts usage, and track the extra parts used as losses. There may also be multiple types of inventory corrections allowed, so that reasons for discrepancies are tracked according to the types of corrections made.

It may be harder to obtain good costs for rework. If regular production employees are charged with doing the rework on unmeasured or 'indirect' time, the costs of rework may have to be estimated. Using the average rework cost per item and the number of reworked items is an appropriate approach if all items' rework costs are similar. At any rate, rework is similar to inspection in that it is something to be eliminated or curtailed.

If the operation seems to require rework, eliminating all rework may sound extreme, but do not let past practice dictate possible outcomes.

Table 4.8 Inventory losses of components.

	Parent item	Component item
Units at start of production	1000	4100
Reported final production	900	
Calculated components used (3 to 1)		1800
Calculated inventory level (start less usage)		2300
Actual parts used (input from machine)		4005
Actual inventory level		95
Inventory correction		*(2205)*

Sometimes current practices are followed simply because no one has looked at root causes or thought creatively about the process. Be sure the rework is really needed. Only if the rework is truly a necessary step in the operation (under current constraints) should you set up a measurement program for your rework. A temporary measurement system may be all that is needed. You will benefit from an accurate measure of rework costs, even if the measure is imprecise. In other words, the costs of rework should be measured in a way that is correct on average, even if the actual costs vary from the measured costs from time to time.

Extra Shipping Charges

With the need to make quick decisions, use of overnight or expedited shipping is common. If something goes wrong, these charges can increase rapidly. Measuring the portion of expedited shipping charges due to poor quality may be worthwhile in many operations.

Special Credits to Partners, Suppliers, or Customers

There are situations where customers sustain costs over a period of time due to delivery or product problems. In these cases, your organization may provide them with periodic credits. These credits can be substantial if the customers are important and the problems are large. These credits are not often handled in the same accounts as other failure costs. If this is the situation in your organization, these may need to be considered as a special cost source.

This type of situation may happen less frequently with partners or suppliers. Some examples may include:

- Unsold seasonal product returned by a customer after the selling season.

- Late deliveries to a customer resulting in missed sales.

- Occasional defective product accumulated by a customer for a quarterly credit.

- Costs incurred by a partner due to your organization's subpar performance during a shared project.

- Added costs incurred by a supplier when product specifications from your organization are changed. If these costs increase the initial contracted cost, and your supplier insists on payments to cover their expense, then these added costs of failure are fair game.

Table 4.9 Expected value calculations.

Cost to replace a roof	$10,000
Months between occurrence of hailstorms	120
Monthly expected value of roof replacement due to hailstorm	$83

Using Expected Values

One concept that can help is often called *expected values*. This is appropriate where issues occur on an infrequent basis, but their costs are large when they occur. Sometimes warranty claims will fall into this area, but there may be larger issues such as lawsuits from dissatisfied customers or other considerations in countries with unstable political situations.

An example from personal life would be hail damage to your roof. Hail falls on an irregular basis, but chances are likely that during your ownership of a house, your roof will be damaged by a hailstorm. You can calculate the expected value of the damage on an annual basis even if the incidence is perhaps once every 10 years. You take the probability of occurrence each year (or month, whatever your reporting time period is) and multiply this by the cost when it occurs. Once in every 10 years would be once out of 120 months, and if the cost were $10,000, the expected value on any given month would be $10,000 ÷ 120 or about $83 (see Table 4.9). The probabilities used in this calculation would need to be reviewed on a regular basis or when some instance dictates a change.

Chargeback Systems

A chargeback system can be described as one where losses found in one area are moved or reported as if they had been found in the area where they were caused. Some more sophisticated accounting or costing systems may have a way to do this built in. While these systems can result in beneficial actions, they often have unintended consequences. Here are two ground rules for using this data in a cost of quality report:

- *Maintain a minimum cost where a chargeback is to be used.* Too often, very small costs that occur on a regular basis can end up in this system, and the area on the receiving end of the costs will become deadened to the need to solve the problems.

- *Use this type of system where the causal area is under a different management structure than the finding area.* If the two areas belong to one authority, then use the existing organization structure to make the corrective actions stick. On the other hand, if the two areas belong to two distant organizational entities, then the formal chargeback process may be necessary to highlight the size of the losses and obtain action on a cooperative scale.

Losses at an operation may consist of three types: loss from prior operations found here, loss created here and found here at the time of the operation, and loss created here but found at a later operation.

Manual Corrections

All data systems will fail. Quoting Finagles law: "Anything that can go wrong will go wrong." In accounting systems, effort is expended to avoid this, but there will be times when the reported costs will display errors of sufficient size to obscure the desired results of the report. In these cases, simply reporting the erroneous results will undermine the trust in the cost of quality report. There are three options:

1. Leave the error in, and hope that someone fixes it soon

2. Try and guess what the correct values should be and substitute them in place of the error

3. Remove the data that appears to be in error so that the change is neutral with regard to the goal

If you choose options 2 or 3, you will need to keep track of the corrections. A spreadsheet can do this and allow the recording of key information along with the amount of the correction. The key information needed includes:

- Amount of the correction

- Data source being corrected

- Area of your organization affected by the change

- Cost of quality category affected (prevention, appraisal, failure)

- Expiration date of the correction (if this is a temporary correction)

5

Selling the Idea of Measuring Quality Costs

KNOWING WHAT MAKES FOR SUCCESS

In the Association for the Advancement of Cost Engineering International (AACEI) Skills and Knowledge handbook, Gary Cokins states:

> The rationale for implementing cost of quality is based on the following logic:
>
> - For any failure, there is a root cause.
>
> - Causes for failure are preventable.
>
> - Prevention is cheaper than fixing problems after they occur.
>
> If you accept the logic that it is always less expensive to do the job right the first time than to do it over, the rationale and goal for quality management and using COQ to provide a quality program with concrete and fact-based data should be apparent.[1]

This thought should be kept in mind when you sell a quality costs program. While you will have to adapt your approach based on your specific organization, there are several general points to consider.

Tie-In with Overall Strategy

To start with, look at the strategic initiatives in your organization. What are they? They might involve core business functions, increasing the pace that new products are developed, produced, and marketed, or acquisition of additional portions of the supply chain to increase control over more of the end-to-end process of production. Whatever the strategic initiatives are, by linking quality cost measurements to these initiatives you will enhance the chance that executives will be interested.

Be creative. Since quality costs have a hard-dollar impact on the bottom line, they can easily be linked to most global or strategic plans. The advantage in doing this is that your proposal (stated in synchrony with one or several key goals of your organization) will resonate with senior managers' current concerns.

Push or Pull Selling

In *push selling,* an idea is promoted via direct conversations or presentations. In this approach, you bring up the subject with key decision makers in your organization. Another approach may be termed *pull selling,* where you gradually build support for the program from multiple conversations at several management levels that create links between issues or initiatives and the proposed quality cost program. These discussions are not usually about a quality cost program directly but rather about issues that a quality cost program would help in solving. You may also implement a series of measurements that drive specific organizational improvement and cost savings. Nothing sells better than success. As time goes by, the expectation is that someone in a key decision-making role will recognize the link between your conversation and the demonstrated success and recognize the need for quality cost measurements. These two modes are not mutually exclusive, but you need to know how your organization's culture will react to either approach.

Key Success Factors to Selling

• *Ensure linkage to performance.* Provide a "What's in it for me?" message. Management must see the benefit of using the metrics. What is the urgency?

Be sure the bullet points for your project cover the key performance indicators of your organization. Too many proposals do not link to existing measures. Without this, you will find selling a new program to be difficult or impossible. See the discussion above about a tie-in with overall strategy.

• *Target areas of concern (cost, profit).* Costs and profits are usually of primary concern in organizations. If your organization is not-for-profit, you will have cost control as an important issue, and you may have other cost measures such as return on assets.

• *Provide references, background.* This can be difficult with quality costs. To find any firm willing to disclose publicly the costs of their mistakes is a rare occurrence. You may have to do a pilot study at your organization and have the accounting group standing by to affirm that your pilot is real before you can have real data to sell a program to your leadership.

• *Be prepared to pilot.* You may need a pilot program to collect data that appears applicable to your organization. This need not be an extensive project. In most firms, quality costs are so prevalent that you can find them by scratching the surface of almost any operating area. Look for a department that is receptive to this type of exposure.

• *Look for "enthusiasts" and/or find the natural leaders that drive the internal processes.* Others will take their cues from them. If leaders agree and support the activity, others will follow.

A receptive person may be a new manager, one who won't be blamed for mistakes that occurred before he or she was appointed to their position. In every organization there is always someone who gets it, who understands the concept intuitively. Help them and they will be your champion.

You should look for a department that is important to the organization. A support operation on the periphery will not make a good case. You will also need to choose an area where prevention activities, inspection activities, and failure events can be tied to one another. This will make the case for prevention much more compelling.

• *Finance/accounting support.* Your accounting group must be an active supporter of your plan. A quality manager may not have the credentials to talk about costs with senior managers in many firms. The senior executives will look to the accounting group for confirmation of your proposal. If the accounting group is your partner you will have their support.

• *Put together a sample report.* This can be a simple mock-up or it can use data from a trial run of a quality cost system in your organization.

THE DREAM TEAM: YOU AND ACCOUNTING

In making your proposal, quality and accounting should be partners. However, their roles are different. Whoever is championing the method (the quality, engineering, or operations representative) will likely be the subject matter expert. He or she needs to be able to talk about both quality and cost. The champion should keep the focus on the improvement process, with the quality cost program as the driving force behind process improvement. You should have an idea of how the various quality improvement methodologies work at your organization before you sell a quality cost program, as the question is likely to come up in your discussion with top executives, "Why would we add this alternative cost measurement program if we already do Six Sigma (or lean or ISO or Baldrige, or whatever)?" Quality costs measurements complement these programs by making costs more visible and will drive good management practices.

The accounting department should provide focus on the balance sheet or the profit and loss statement, or other key measures of financial health. Accounting can vouch for the accuracy of the quality cost methodology and the resulting measurements. They will also know how costs flow through your organization and how costs are allocated, spread, or assigned. The accounting structure will determine the methods you should use to collect the quality cost data.

PRESENTING TO TOP EXECUTIVES

Your senior executives are the ultimate decision authority. If your organization is large, there are probably several layers of middle managers that you need to convince before you talk to top executives. These mid-level managers are gatekeepers and one of their functions is to weed out trivial information that top managers don't need to hear.

If your organization is small, you may know the top executives already. If you do, you still must be prepared to discuss alignment of the quality cost program with key objectives.

No matter how large or small the organization, senior executives converse in the language of finance, the language of money: profit and loss, costs, revenues, and so on. You have to make your case using the same language.

DO'S AND DON'TS

Be sure to illustrate both a problem and a solution. Make your points with as few words as possible while making them clearly. Keep your primary points to three or less. Try taking an outside perspective while using key themes that resonate within your organization. Remember to state "what's in it for me" from your senior executive's point of view. See Table 5.1.

Table 5.1 Do's and don'ts for executive presentations.

Do	Don't
Explain financial benefits	Explain all the details of a quality cost program
Understand key points of current strategic initiatives and link the quality cost program to these	List any possible quality department benefits
Show genuine concern for the overall organization	Use a too-slick, polished, overly-rehearsed, and elaborate presentation
Demonstrate how each part of the organization benefits; accounting, operations, and quality are the key business areas	Talk about long-term benefit while ignoring short-term impact

A Business-Related Sample Report

One concern that may or may not be evident at your organization is the need to coordinate between different areas of the firm. While this is most likely to occur in a larger organization, smaller ones may have difficulties with it as well. When different areas of the organization operate independently there can be problems between these 'silos' of activity.

For example, let's explore the scenario where your sales/marketing group feels the need to have something different in the marketplace. Your existing products are getting old. The sales group places pressure on leadership, who hands the task to your product development area. The product development group then exercises their creative juices, several new products are developed, and the operations group begins to produce them. If the sales group is not involved prior to ramping up for volume production, the new products may have little or no real market. After all, the development group may not have access to all the customers that are known to use existing or potential new products.

A quality cost program, however, should be measuring the various expenses that occur when products are produced but not sold. Discards, obsolescence, returns from the field, and loss of goodwill all represent a lack of prevention activities that focus on avoiding the mass production of unneeded products. If such a program is in place, both the product development area and the sales area are held accountable for overall performance, and they can clearly see what will result if they don't communicate at key points in the product development process. Therefore, the quality cost model makes something very clear that a simple profit and loss statement would not—the connection between specific prevention activities and specific failure costs.

To convert this to the language of finance, examine the quality cost report in Figure 5.1 and the sample profit and loss statement in Figure 5.2, with quality costs indicated. (This example has been simplified to help illustrate the procedure.)

Quality costs may not seem compatible with a profit and loss statement, but they do appear there. External failure costs include the costs from discards, obsolescence, and returns from the field as noted in Figure 5.2 under cost of sales. External failure also may have warranty costs (allocated to the legal and accounting line) and added advertising costs due to problems recognized by customers.

Internal failure would affect both labor costs and materials costs, shown in the wages and supplies lines.

Appraisal and prevention costs are likely to occur primarily in salaries and wages.

The example does not show any future-oriented quality cost, such as lost sales from defecting customers.

Note that the profit and loss statement does not make the link clear that increasing prevention salaries can reduce cost of sales (the discards). Not only are these two costs in different areas of the P&L statement, they occur in different organizational silos.

The quality cost report makes the connection clear. You should make this point when selling your quality cost program to top leaders.

Quality cost report	
Prevention	$ 1
Appraisal	$ 4
Internal failure	$ 7
External failure	$ 9
Total	$21

Figure 5.1 Example quality cost report.

Profit and loss statement		Location of quality costs
Income		
Total net sales	$100	
Cost of sales	$ 12	< External failure: $6
Gross profit	$ 88	
Expenses		
Fixed expenses		
Rent	$ 2	
Utilities	$ 1	
Equipment leases	$ 1	
Depreciation	$ 1	
Insurance	$ 1	
License/permits	$ 1	
Loan payments	$ 2	
Total fixed expenses	$ 9	
Controllable expenses		
Salaries/wages	$ 53	< Appraisal, prevention, internal failure: $10
Payroll expenses	$ 5	
Supplies	$ 10	< Internal failure: $2
Advertising	$ 3	< External failure: $1
Legal and accounting	$ 4	< External failure: $2
Total controllable expenses	$ 75	
Total expenses	$ 84	
Net profit (loss)	$ 4	
Taxes	$ 1	
Net profit after taxes	$ 3	

Figure 5.2   Example profit and loss statement.

PRESENTING TO OPERATIONS AND MIDDLE MANAGEMENT

If your organization is large, you will need to make presentations to middle managers. Some of the above techniques are useful there as well, but there are other specifics to consider. First, middle managers will be thinking what's in it for me (WIIFM)? This WIIFM tendency is a major factor and you should think about how quality costs affect the specific areas controlled by the managers you are addressing. Many middle managers are also concerned how the identification of the cost of mistakes will be viewed by those above them in the organization.

To counter these concerns, you can stress how measuring quality costs will help managers. For example, a production manager may be having difficulties in making monthly production quotas. The amount of rework may be a problem; if so, focus the discussion on how a larger prevention budget (more training, engineers, or planners) can be justified to prevent the rework and raise real production output without adding space or new machines. Show managers something that will make them look good. Speak in terms of operational measures: preventing defects from occurring, moving appraisal to earlier points in the flow, establishing better tolerances within operational processes, and so on.

Some middle managers may speak the language of finance, some may be more comfortable with operations measures such as defective parts per million, others may use both types of measures. Know your audience.

MAKING A SUPERIOR PRESENTATION

These six general guidelines to making a formal presentation will help you gain acceptance:

1. Lay out the current condition; not the obvious facts, but a statement focused on the primary problems on which the current business/improvement initiatives are intended to focus. Indicate which of these primary problems a quality cost program will help solve.

2. Using information gained from background discussions with various managers, explain what the measure of success of the quality cost program will be. Reiterate the value to the organization of implementing quality costs. List both financial benefits and nonmeasured benefits, the hidden costs of quality. Tie quality costs to improvement activities.

3. Lay out implementation options: a pilot program, an annual check, a quarterly measurement system, and/or a monthly reporting system. Keep the list to three or four options that

make sense, keeping in mind what the top executives will support. Having options to choose from is always more inviting than being told exactly what to do.

4. Indicate how long it will take to implement the program with the available resources, covering all the options listed.

5. Explain joint accountabilities. List what will be needed from each department or division and how these resources and timing play out for each option. Use a table if needed.

6. Ask for acceptance. This may be delayed if you have insufficient understanding of the thinking of the managers. Getting acceptance right away is best; otherwise, try to fix a date for a final decision.

DEALING WITH OPPOSITION

There may be significant opposition to your proposal. Don't wait until you encounter resistance; try and find out what it may be and where it may come from and then brainstorm ways to avoid, circumvent, or remove the basis for the opposition. Just because you are convinced of the proposal's value, others may feel entirely justified in their own concerns. Take these approaches:

- Assess risks and be prepared to address them.

- Use a noncompete approach with colleagues and assure them you are looking for a win/win solution.

- Try to find the natural owners and leaders—those that have the most to gain. Work with them to get buy-in.

- Point out how much infrastructure your organization already has—a cost accounting system, transactional data, feedback from external failures, and so on. By using this existing infrastructure, a quality cost program can be implemented with minimal expense. Using the existing data and processes will increase the return from the activities already under way.

Often managers are looking to find a lever that will allow them to move their organization in a better direction. Point out that a quality cost system is a behavior modification tool. Actually, all forms of measurement will encourage one kind of behavior or another; they are all behavior modification tools. View it like this: by measuring only a budget and rewarding budget reductions, budgets are reduced, even if it hurts the functioning of an organization. You will get the behavior rewarded by your measure. Quality cost measures done well will link cause to effect and encourage prevention behaviors.

6

Quality Costs Gone Wrong—It Can Be a Minefield

T here are ways to do quality costs measurements and improvements right, and there are ways to do them wrong. While not every approach will work at every organization, there are some things that are just bad ideas. In this chapter we will cover some of the problem areas that can come up in establishing and operating a cost of quality program.

DISHONESTY, PROCESSES, AND MEASUREMENT

Managers and supervisors often face an apparent dichotomy in rewarding employee behavior—should they support quality of work or should they support honesty when an employee identifies a mistake? Understanding that both are desirable, these two goals can be in conflict. On one hand, it feels natural to put full emphasis on recognizing employees that rarely make mistakes. But this could persuade employees to avoid reporting their mistakes. Not reporting mistakes is further encouraged if the organization has an inspection program that lets the employee pass along mistakes without suffering consequences. An employee may take the view that mistakes will be removed by the inspectors and will not result in a problem for customers. Never underestimate the human ability to find justification for action (or inaction)!

How do you keep honesty in the forefront and still recognize highly skilled employees whose mistakes occur less frequently?

One approach is to separate the two recognition processes. Reward employees for high performance at a different time and place, and in a different manner, than discussing mistakes and solutions for errors. Clearly, discussing mistakes and errors in an atmosphere of highly charged emotion will not help with building improvement. We should seek solutions when errors are discovered, not punishment.

Keeping cost of quality reporting in an atmosphere of root cause analysis and focusing on fixing underlying issues will help keep blame from driving employees to hide their mistakes. The desired state of learning from our mistakes can be a hard road to follow. If an organization has been immersed in a climate of holding people responsible for systemic issues (as blame is often called) it will take considerable time and effort to change the mindset of employees. It is here that support from the top and firm guidance by all levels of management are absolutely essential in making a cost of quality program a success. It doesn't just happen. It takes focused effort.

A second approach that may help is distinguishing between two types of errors—accidental and intentional. Since anyone can have an off day, this may not always be clear in any one instance. It may take more than one instance to determine whether an employee is intentionally letting some problem happen, the problem was accidental and unavoidable, or just part of working in a broken process.

A third approach that helps with error analysis is what W. Edwards Deming called *common cause* versus *special cause*. Common cause errors are driven by the structure of the process itself. Common cause errors represent variation built into raw materials, machine fluctuations, or process flow. Special cause variation errors may be due to employees not following a process, using the wrong materials, or some unusual outside influence. Deming said that 94 percent of process problems come from common cause errors driven by the original process design.

A fourth approach is to set up group measures. Determine what measures are important in the performance of a work group. This approach helps employees see that their mistakes are not just a problem for a faceless customer, but affect the people they work with daily. By using group measures, employees are encouraged to help one another avoid problems. Performance measures that are entirely based on individual measurement will inevitably lead to less team learning on the job and encourage some employees to maximize their personal success even where it hurts the overall output of the team. Individual measures set up a win/lose scenario. Group measures help set up a win/win scenario.

By combining these four approaches, a solution to dishonesty can be put in place in most organizations.

TOO COMPLEX AND TOO SIMPLE SYSTEMS

Organizations often have large and overly complex systems. They also may take a simplistic view and leave important details out of their systems architecture. Complex systems may be called sophisticated and allow for control of market situations. Simple approaches are quick to deploy and allow for rapid action to make the most out of a changing marketplace. The detail level of an organization's systems needs to be determined by the organization's overall goals and current situation.

The cost of quality program should be kept as simple as possible to allow visibility for action. If the process of measuring cost of quality is too complex, few will understand the system and clever employees will find some way to hide quality costs. If the process is too simple, however, insufficient detail will be available to direct change. Those close to the problem areas will know when details are insufficient for driving action. Listen to your local experts.

If the system needs to have a high level of complexity to show trends and direct efforts, then management must ensure that knowledge of this system is maintained as employees rotate through jobs. By maintaining broad, in-depth knowledge of the system there can be a high degree of self-policing to keep distortions to a minimum.

If your organization has a highly complex system for tracking losses, there will be so many loss categories and methods to record them that clever but unscrupulous employees will find ways to hide losses.

CHARGEBACK PROCEDURES

As mentioned earlier, a chargeback process is one where losses found in one area are moved or reported as if they had been found in the area where they were caused. Such systems often do more harm than good. When an employee has charged a problem to another area, they no longer have an interest in finding a solution to the root cause of the problem, or even designing a work-around in their own area.

Figure 6.1 shows a typical operation and three losses. Moving left to right, "prior operation loss found here" indicates the losses covered in this discussion. The next two losses, "This operation loss found here" and "This operation loss (found later)" are quality costs, but not chargebacks.

At the same time, the area receiving the charge now has to deal with this transaction that arrives out of nowhere and may refer to work that they

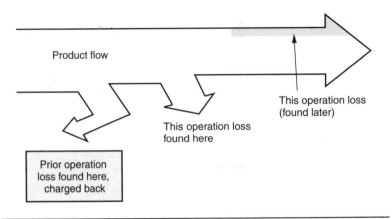

Product flow

This operation loss
(found later)

This operation loss
found here

Prior operation
loss found here,
charged back

Figure 6.1   Chargeback loss in flow.

did months before. They are busy with today's work, and what happened months ago is of little importance. If there is a purchasing arrangement where the supplier–customer relationship recognizes these charges, and if the charges get large enough that some future work is as risk, the receiving area may act to correct some of the problems.

The issue is twofold:

- The downstream area believes that the problems are solved when they make the chargeback.

- The upstream area sees the problems as low in importance. After all, if the upstream area did not identify the cost and seek to reduce it before it left their area, then it must not be a big problem.

The result is no improvement. If you implement such a system, use the ground rules in Chapter 4, pages 61–62.

Large cost problems may be treated with a chargeback approach, but they will need to be truly large if there is to be action. Also, it must not be too easy to create a chargeback system transaction; this will make the problem more visible to all concerned. The key to rapid correction of multistep process issues is face-to-face communication between those at the working level of the business. If you use a chargeback system, be sure your system does not end up isolating people and hurting the face-to-face communication you want to take place.

Not charging back latent problems does not mean to avoid measuring them, knowing their impact on the current operation, and analyzing them.

Even if you do not charge back costs, if latent issues are significant, using a Pareto chart to distinguish the significant few from the insignificant many is a necessary step. You may then have a factual basis with which to engage people in the face-to-face discussions that lead to true resolution of the root causes of the latent problems.

MANUAL CORRECTION OF DATA

Many data errors are small and are either fixed quickly or go unnoticed. This is not an issue. Every now and then there will be a larger data error. When this error gets to the cost of quality report, there will be those who blame the cost of quality system for the problem. In the best scenario, some managers will question the cost of quality system, and improvement activities will be slowed or stopped. A large data glitch may cause the results of improvement actions to be hidden, or worse yet, exaggerated!

To avoid a poor reaction to the data glitch, there will need to be some way to correct (even temporarily) the data error within the cost of quality reports.

Having the ability to fix problems offers the opportunity to easily improve on the data fed from regular sources. While such action may begin with good intentions, the number of corrections will continue to increase. Such manual fixes will seem inexpensive, but issues are created as the fixes grow. Like laws passed by a well-meaning legislature, nothing is ever removed.

There are four steps to keeping this under control:

1. Set limits on the allowable magnitude of corrections. Keeping corrections for only the larger issues will prevent small instances from becoming overwhelming.

2. Keep management aware of the correction frequency and magnitude of corrections. There can be an out-of-sight, out-of-mind situation where the corrections remain invisible since the final reports perform satisfactorily.

3. Replace or overhaul buggy systems. Some systems will generate more than their share of problems. At some point, these systems should be overhauled or replaced.

4. Employees providing input into these systems may need periodic retraining to prevent the garbage-in, garbage-out syndrome.

LOSS VALUATION

Some organizations' cost accounting systems operate as if there is no such thing as in-process loss. They take the final, completed quantity and divide it into the total expenditures to make the product. This is the cost of completed product; it is correct as far as it goes. It leaves open the question of the value of the product components that are lost along the way. The lost components and materials are not free; also, they are not worth the full cost of the final product. Additionally, they are not worth merely the cost of the material itself. There are both labor and material costs in the in-process losses. To manage this loss, some kind of estimate is needed to value the lost in-process components and materials.

If possible, this estimate can be created from the cumulative costs and the completed components at each stage of production. For example, Table 6.1 is a chart of steps from a work order, showing quantity completed at each step, the added costs for each step, and the loss occurring at each step.

The total cost of the 600 completed parts is $185. Now by adding each cost to all previous costs, a cumulative cost is generated. Multiplying the spoilage quantity by the cumulative cost and adding the result provides an estimate of the spoilage costs. See Table 6.2.

Table 6.1 Spoilage quantity.

Step	Quantity completed	Cost added	Spoilage quantity
1	900	$ 10	100
2	850	$ 75	50
3	600	$100	250
Total	600	$185	400

Table 6.2 Spoilage cost.

Step	Quantity completed	Cost added	Cumulative cost	Cumulative cost per unit	Spoilage quantity	Spoilage cost estimate
1	900	$ 10	$ 10	$0.011	100	$ 1.11
2	850	$ 75	$ 85	$0.100	50	$ 5.00
3	600	$100	$185	$0.308	250	$77.08
Total	600	$185			400	$83.19

Such a method shows that simply identifying losses earlier in the process may reduce the cost of quality by a significant margin. Defective product passed downstream for later identification will increase the cost of quality.

If the costing system valued the losses at the cost of the first step, the total cost of loss would have been estimated at $4.44, instead of the true cost of $83.19. Valuing loss at the final unit cost of $0.308 would estimate the total loss cost at $133, again an incorrect number. Using the earliest cost or the final cost will not make visible the savings achieved if defective parts were found and discarded at an earlier step. Also, costs do not accrue in a linear manner from start to finish. Using cumulative stepwise costs to value spoilage during the process will provide the best picture of quality costs.

For most cases, the valuation does not have to be so precise that parts found to be spoiled before each step are valued at the previous step's cumulative cost, and those found at the end of each step's processing are valued at that step's cumulative cost.

Having a costing system that produces significantly correct loss costs is important, but if your organization is small, this type of costing system may not be possible. You will need to use what you have as best as you can.

KEEP IT TOP OF MIND (OR NEAR THE TOP)

Savings can begin in weeks or months, but a cost of quality program can take up to 10 years before it starts showing a diminishing rate of return (see Figure 6.2). During this time, there will be changes in managers.

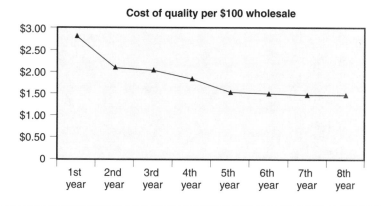

Figure 6.2 Typical eight-year improvement trend.

Overall goals of your organization may change, so keeping the cost of quality visible and understood may require annual (or more often) selling to new managers.

One key ingredient in the process of keeping the program going is to have the accounting area create and deliver the quality cost report. Sell the program throughout the organization, but if possible have the accounting group prepare the reports. The accounting area in most organizations is a service group and does not usually promote individual programs. The quality and operations groups, on the other hand, will be able to demonstrate the positive benefits the cost of quality program continues to provide. A key to keeping the program vital is to link the cost of quality to positive outcomes. Since quality is most often associated with negative issues, this linking to positives is a necessary step.

As your cost of quality program gets to be several years old and the improvements start to show diminishing returns, a renewal will be in order. The costs identified as significant at the beginning may have been shrunk to the point where they are no longer. If so, count yourself fortunate.

You can renew your program by looking at some of the hidden cost areas that may have been passed over at the start. These hidden costs, not measured previously, may have been reduced as a by-product of the quality cost program, but it is worthwhile to confirm this. If significant hidden costs are found, the quality cost program can be renewed to address them.

Appendix A
Examples of Cost of Quality Measurements

1.0 PREVENTION[1]

1.1 Marketing/Customer/User

- 1.1.1 Marketing Research—determinations of customer quality needs, product or service attributes to provide a high degree of satisfaction.

- 1.1.2 Customer/User Perception Surveys—programs to determine customer expectations and needs.

- 1.1.3 Contract/Document Review—review and evaluation of customer contracts affecting actual product or service requirements.

1.2 Product/Service/Design Development

- 1.2.1 Design Quality Progress Reviews—planning and execution of tasks to maximize conformance to customer needs prior to release in production.

- 1.2.2 Design Support Activities—document checking, selection of components, risk analyses for product safety, FMEA activities, customer misuse analysis, overall quality management planning.

- 1.2.3 Product Design Qualification Test—planning and conducting tests to qualify new products and major changes to current products.

- 1.2.4 Service Design Qualification—planning and performing tests of new or changed service processes.

- 1.2.5 Field Trials—planned observations and evaluation of end-product performance in trial situations.

1.3 Purchasing Prevention Costs

- 1.3.1 Supplier Reviews—surveys to review and evaluate individual suppliers' capabilities to meet quality requirements.

- 1.3.2 Supplier Rating—developing and maintaining a system to ascertain each supplier's continued acceptability.

- 1.3.3 Purchase Order Tech Data Reviews—assuring that transmitted technical data will communicate requirements to suppliers.

- 1.3.4 Supplier Quality Planning—planning for the incoming and source inspections and tests necessary to determine acceptance of supplier products.

1.4 Operations (Manufacturing or Service) Prevention Costs

- 1.4.1 Operations Process Validation—assuring that new methods, processes, equipment, machinery, and tools will perform to required limits.

- 1.4.2 Operations Quality Planning—development of necessary product or service inspection, test, and audit procedures, appraisal documentation system, and workmanship or appearance standards to assure continued achievement of acceptable quality results.

  – 1.4.2.1 Design and Development of Quality Measurement and Control Equipment—test equipment engineers, planners, and designers, gage engineers, inspection equipment engineers, planners, and designers.

- 1.4.3 Operations Support Quality Planning—activities to support quality control to the production process.

- 1.4.4 Operator Quality Education—development and conduct of formal operator training programs for the express purpose of preventing errors.

- 1.4.5 Operator SPC/Process Control—education to implement statistical process control.

1.5 Quality Administration

- 1.5.1 Administrative Salaries—quality function managers, directors, supervisors, and clerical.

- 1.5.2 Administrative Expenses—office expense for quality functions.

- 1.5.3 Quality Program Planning—manual development and maintenance, inputs to proposals, quality record keeping, strategic planning, and budget control.

- 1.5.4 Quality Performance Reporting—quality data collection, analysis, and reporting supporting continued improvement (for example, quality cost reporting).

- 1.5.5 Quality Education—initial and continued quality education of all company functions affecting product or service quality to customers.

- 1.5.6 Quality Improvement—development and conduct of companywide quality improvement programs.

- 1.5.7 Quality System Audits—audits performed to observe and evaluate the overall effectiveness of the quality management system and procedures.

2.0 APPRAISAL

2.1 Purchasing Appraisal Costs

- 2.1.1 Receiving or Incoming Inspections—all normal or routine inspection and/or test of purchased materials, products, and services.

- 2.1.2 Measurement Equipment—acquisition (depreciation or expense), calibration, and maintenance of measurement or process control equipment.

- 2.1.3 Qualification of Supplier Product—added inspections or tests on production quantities for periodic qualification.

- 2.1.4 Source Inspection and Control Programs—all costs (including travel) to conduct 2.1.1 or 2.1.3 at the supplier's plant or an independent test laboratory.

2.2 Operations (Manufacturing or Service) Appraisal Costs

- 2.2.1 Planned Operations Inspections, Tests, Audits.

  – 2.2.1.1 Checking Labor—production operator's time to check their work.

  – 2.2.1.2 Product or Service Quality Audits—labor to provide in-process or finished product quality audits.

  – 2.2.1.3 Inspection and Test Materials—materials consumed in control of quality.

- 2.2.2 Setup Inspections and Tests—all setup or first-piece inspections and tests used to assure that each combination of machine and tool is properly adjusted to produce acceptable products before the start of each production lot.

- 2.2.3 Special Tests (Manufacturing)—nonroutine inspections and tests as part of the appraisal plan.

- 2.2.4 Process Control Measurements—all planned measures and adjustments of processing equipment or materials to assure or maintain conformance to standards.

- 2.2.5 Laboratory Support—cost of lab tests in support of appraisal.

- 2.2.6 Measurement Equipment—acquisition (depreciation or expense), calibration, and maintenance of measurement or process control equipment.

  – 2.2.6.1 Depreciation Allowances—for capitalized appraisal equipment.

  – 2.2.6.2 Measurement Equipment Expenses—noncapitalized acquisition cost.

  – 2.2.6.3 Maintenance and Calibration Labor—all inspections, calibration, maintenance, and control of appraisal equipment, instruments, and gages used for evaluation of process, products, or services for conformance to requirements.

- 2.2.7 Outside Endorsements and Certifications—required endorsement or certifications. Includes sample preparation and submittal and liaison costs.

2.3 External Appraisal Costs

- 2.3.1 Field Performance Evaluations—all appraisal efforts (inspections, tests, audits, and appraisal support activities) planned and conducted at the site for installation and/or delivery of large, complex products or the conduct of merchandised services.

- 2.3.2 Special Product Evaluations—life testing, environmental and reliability tests on production units.

- 2.3.3 Evaluation of Field Stock and Spare Parts—testing and inspection of field stock for storage time, engineering changes, or other suspected problems.

2.4 Review of Test and Inspection Data

Regularly reviewing inspection and test data prior to shipment release.

2.5 Miscellaneous Quality Evaluations

Evaluations to assure nonproduction departments' ability to provide acceptable support to production.

3.0 INTERNAL FAILURE

3.1 Product/Service Design Failure Costs (Internal)

- 3.1.1 Design Corrective Action—postproduction release investigation and redesign to resolve problems inherent in the design.

- 3.1.2 Rework Due to Design Changes—rework materials, labor, and burden costs to resolve problems due to postproduction design changes.

- 3.1.3 Scrap Due to Design Changes—total cost of scrap due to postproduction design changes.

- 3.1.4 Production Liaison Costs—unplanned support to production due to inadequate or incomplete design instructions.

3.2 Purchasing Failure Costs

- 3.2.1 Purchased Material Reject Disposition Costs—disposal or sorting of incoming inspection rejects, including reject documentation, review and evaluation, disposition orders, handling, and transportation.

- 3.2.2 Purchased Material Replacement Costs—added cost of replacing rejected and returned items (not paid for by the supplier).

- 3.2.3 Supplier Corrective Action—company-sponsored failure analyses and investigations into the cause of supplier rejects to determine necessary corrective actions; includes cost of visits to supplier locations for this purpose and cost to provide necessary added inspection protection while the problem is being resolved.

- 3.2.4 Rework of Supplier Rejects—repair expense not billed to the supplier, usually due to production expediency.

- 3.2.5 Uncontrolled Material Losses—materials shortages due to damage, theft, or unknown reasons.

3.3 Operations Failure Costs

- 3.3.1 Material Review and Corrective Action Costs—review, disposition, and correction of nonconforming products or services, with preventive actions.

  - 3.3.1.1 Disposition Costs—review and disposition of nonconforming product or service.

  - 3.3.1.2 Troubleshooting or Failure Analysis Costs—failure analysis (physical, chemical, and so forth) conducted by, or obtained from, outside laboratories in support of defect cause identification.

  - 3.3.1.3 Investigation Support Costs—test runs or designed experiments to obtain and solve a particular problem.

  - 3.3.1.4 Operations Corrective Action—corrective actions taken to remove or eliminate the root causes of nonconformances identified for correction; includes rewriting operator instructions, redevelopment of processes or procedures, redesign or modification of equipment or tooling, and development and implementation of specific training needs.

- 3.3.2 Operations Rework and Repair Costs—labor, material, and overhead associated with rework or repair of defective product or service discovered within the operations process.

  – 3.3.2.1 Rework—material, labor, and burden for all work done to bring nonconforming product or service up to an acceptable condition.

  – 3.3.2.2 Repair—material, labor, and burden for all work done to bring nonconforming product up to an acceptable or equivalent, but still nonconforming, condition.

- 3.3.3 Reinspection/Retest Costs—that portion of inspection, test, and audit labor that is incurred because of rejects; includes documentation of rejects, reinspection or test after rework/repair, and sorting of defective lots.

- 3.3.4 Extra Operations.

- 3.3.5 Scrap Costs—material, labor, and overhead for defective product or service that is wasted or disposed of because it can not be reworked to conform to requirements.

- 3.3.6 Downgraded End Product or Service—price differential between normal selling price and reduced selling price due to nonconforming or off-grade end products or services because of quality reasons.

- 3.3.7 Internal Failure Labor Losses—lost labor due to nonconforming work.

4.0 EXTERNAL FAILURE

- 4.1 Complaint Investigations/Customer or User Service— investigating, resolving, and responding to individual customer or user complaints or inquiries, including necessary field service.

- 4.2 Returned Goods—evaluating and repairing or replacing goods not meeting acceptance by the customer or user due to quality problems.

- 4.3 Retrofit Costs—costs for modification or updating of products or facilities caused by design deficiencies and resultant quality problems.

  – 4.3.1 Recall Costs—recall activity due to quality problems.

- 4.4 Warranty Claims—claims paid to the customer or user, after acceptance, to cover expenses, including repair costs such as removing defective hardware from a system or cleaning costs due to a food or chemical service accident.

- 4.5 Liability Costs—liability claims, including the cost of product or service liability insurance.

- 4.6 Penalties—contractual or governmental payments due to lowered product or service performance.

- 4.7 Customer/User Goodwill—costs incurred, over and above normal selling costs, to customers or users who are not completely satisfied with the quality of a delivered product or service, such as costs incurred because customers' quality expectations are greater than what they received.

- 4.8 Lost Sales—value of contribution margin lost due to sales reduction because of quality problems.

Appendix B
Case Studies

CASE STUDY #1:
QUALITY COSTS IN A BANK[1]

Charles A. Aubrey, II, Manager, Quality Assurance
Debra A. Zimbler, Quality Control Analyst
Continental Illinois National Bank and Trust Company of Chicago
Chicago, Illinois

A quality cost study was done in a loan processing section after developing quality costs for the area. The study showed that the activity "processing holdouts," which is defined as computer tickets that are rejected during daily processing, represented failure costs of more than $2000 per month. Holdouts accounted for 30 percent of all tickets processed. In order to reprocess the holdouts, the reason for the reject had to be determined, so the tickets were held for next-day processing. The delay prevented accurate and timely updating of commercial lending information. This information is needed to determine a customer's credit availability, the bank's credit exposure, and the bank's financial statements.

Prior to developing quality costs, the loan processing area had not been aware of the magnitude of their quality costs and, in particular, the holdout problem as evidenced by its high monthly failure cost. The area was enthusiastic about initiating a quality improvement project in an effort to reduce holdouts, lower costs, and increase quality. Since the cause of the excessive number of holdouts was unknown, the quality improvement project began with data collection.

In an effort to identify the problem, the area supervisor kept a holdout log. Each holdout was listed by the type of error that caused the reject, as well as the clerk who submitted it. Pareto analysis was done to determine which errors occurred most frequently and which clerks were responsible for the greatest number of errors. A matrix was constructed to see if there was a correlation between the two.

After completing the Pareto analysis, it was found that three types of errors were primarily responsible for the rejected tickets and that three clerks were responsible for the majority of the errors. The actual production operation was carefully monitored to determine the causes of the high error rates by certain clerks and the different types of errors. Particular attention was paid to the quality of the incoming information and to how the clerk transferred it onto the computer input tickets. Further, the rejected tickets that were resubmitted were monitored to determine if they were again rejected. Since it was the responsibility of the clerk to determine the cause of the initial rejection and correct it, a twice-rejected ticket might indicate that the clerk was unsure as to how to correct the error. It was found that few tickets were rejected twice, which indicated that the clerks knew how to correct a rejected ticket.

Observations identified possible causes of the high error rates that were responsible for the rejected tickets. Frequently, incomplete or unclear information was received. and some of the clerks were unsure as to how to proceed with the processing. Knowing the need for immediacy in processing, the clerks attempted to process the less-than-perfect information. It appeared that there was not a consistent method of completing input tickets since each clerk has his/her own method of completion. Further, since the supervisor had not been closely monitoring the holdouts, she was not giving the clerks necessary feedback or suggesting corrective action for the most frequently occurring errors.

These observations suggested multiple courses of action, which were acted upon. Each clerk was required to participate in a training program in order to ensure a uniform understanding of section and ticket processing procedures. A comprehensive procedures manual was written to accompany the training program and to serve as ready reference for the clerks. Clerks were encouraged to ask the senior clerk or supervisor questions concerning processing of nonroutine items. By asking for clarification up front, prevention and appraisal activities were being performed in order to reduce failure costs later. Additional appraisal activities were now being performed by the clerks. They were instructed to reject input information that was incomplete or unclear and return it to the initiator, instead of attempting to process it and hoping it would "pass." By returning bad input to the user, the loan area was giving the user important feedback regarding their quality. This improved the quality of the input to the loan area.

The analysis had shown that the errors that occurred most frequently were caused by not matching two critical fields on the input ticket. As a result, the training course stressed that the clerks pay particular attention to correctly completing the matching fields.

The supervisor was encouraged to take greater initiative in measuring (sampling) the frequency and types of errors that were occurring as well as giving clerks frequent feedback. By monitoring the types of errors, the frequency, and the person responsible, the supervisor could resolve or correct a potential problem before quality would be severely affected. The frequent feedback made the clerks more aware and more responsible for the quality of their work. Together, the supervisor and clerks worked to attack poor quality symptoms before they became quality problems.

Six months after initially developing quality costs, the costs were reviewed. The suggestions had resulted in a shift of the area's quality cost mix, and a reduction in overall quality costs and total costs, as well as improved quality. The training and feedback increased the prevention and appraisal activities of both the supervisor and the clerks. Failure costs decreased significantly while quality improved, since rejects were virtually eliminated. The time the supervisor spent writing the procedures manual and developing the training were considered one-time costs, while the ongoing training and review of the clerks was considered part of the supervisor's basic responsibilities.

CASE STUDY #2:
USING COST OF QUALITY TO
IMPROVE BUSINESS RESULTS

Susanne Donovan, Director of Quality Systems
CRC Industries
Warminster, Pennsylvania

In 1997 CRC Industries first started tracking cost of quality. Since then we have come to consider it a key measure for improving business results and the foundation of our continuous improvement efforts. As Figure B.1 shows, we have reduced failure dollars—the money we spend because of products and services that do not meet our customers' requirements—from 0.70 percent of sales to 0.21 percent of sales, saving hundreds of thousands of dollars.

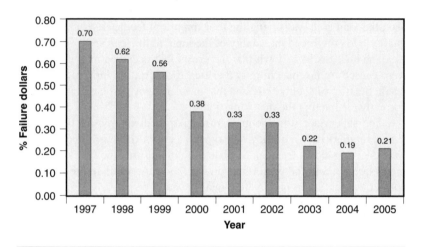

Figure B.1   Failure dollars as a percent of sales.

Of course everyone knows "if you measure it, it will improve," but there was more to our endeavor than simply measuring the results. We crafted a straightforward, but not effortless, process for putting the cost of quality measurement to work for us as a driver of product improvement and, consequently, the company's bottom line.

About CRC Industries

Headquartered in Warminster, Pennsylvania, CRC Industries produces specialty chemicals for maintenance and repair professionals, serving automotive, marine, electrical, industrial, and aviation markets. We have been ISO 9001 certified since November 19, 1996, and in April 2003, independent auditors from Intertek Testing Services confirmed that we successfully upgraded our quality system from ISO 9001:1994 to ISO 9001:2000.

CRC adheres to strict guidelines in all facets of research, development, and production. We believe that our leadership in the maintenance chemical markets is reflected most positively in our product development, and we have committed to a quality policy to meet or exceed customer requirements while complying with statutory and regulatory requirements and ensuring cost-effective operations.

The cost of quality metric therefore seemed like a natural fit for our existing quality policy, but we could not have predicted the full extent of the impact it would have.

What Is Cost of Quality?

Often misinterpreted to mean the cost of using quality methods, cost of quality actually refers to the expense of failing to provide a quality product or service. As described in J. Campanella, *Principles of Quality Costs: Principles, Implementation, and Use,* the total cost of quality includes three types of costs; prevention costs, appraisal costs, and failure costs. Examples of prevention costs include improvement projects, root cause meetings, training, and planning. Appraisal costs include inspection, testing, auditing, and calibration. Failure costs are often divided into two categories, internal and external failure costs. Internal failure costs include scrap, rework, and reinspection costs. External failure costs include customer complaints, warranty claims, and recalls. By increasing preventive costs, companies can reduce failure costs and appraisal costs to the point that the overall total cost of quality is reduced.[2]

At CRC Industries we decided to focus our efforts on tracking failure costs. We took this approach for several reasons:

1. Prevention and appraisal costs are generally more difficult to track and thus more likely to present barriers to getting started.

2. Prevention and appraisal costs are based mainly on labor hours associated with these activities. We did not want employees to view our system as a labor reduction project.

3. Winning buy-in from upper management and employees at all levels is easy when the project involves reducing failure dollars. Everyone can understand the value in reducing waste, rework, and customer complaints.

4. CRC Industries' upper management had bought in to the concept that increasing preventive measures would reduce failure costs. While we did not track prevention costs, we approached reducing failure dollars through increasing our preventive actions.

At CRC Industries, we use the term "failure dollars" to describe the different kinds of expenses—from the cost of materials and labor for rework, to the cost to correct shipping and customer service errors, to the cost of product replacement and waste—that make up the total cost of quality. In centering our improvement efforts on cost of quality, we are not simply focusing on CRC's balance sheet. We are also confronting the issues that keep us from providing the best products and services possible. While reduced costs and increased savings remain the primary benefits we track, we understand that improvements in other quality metrics, such as accuracy, productivity, and customer satisfaction, are tied to cost of quality results.

CRC Industries' Cost of Quality Journey

Recognizing the importance of the cost of quality metric to our overall mission, we set about systematizing our use of the metric as a driver of improvement through the following steps.

1. Establish the Measurement System. Establishing a consistent measuring system required the involvement of various departments within CRC, most importantly our finance department. Specifically, our task was to determine how the data would be collected and what categories would be tracked.

This may seem like an easy step at first, but measurement definitions are not always obvious. Questions we had to address included:

- How do we count costs for returns due to customer errors or customer requests, separating them from returns due to product defects?

- How much does a customer service entry error or shipping error cost?

Before we could begin to collect accurate data, we had to negotiate answers to these questions and many more, and we had to standardize our approach.

2. Collect the Data. To establish a baseline for future improvements, we spent the first year collecting the initial data. During this step, we finalized most of the measure criteria and refined the measurement system. The system developed in 1997 has remained the basis of our cost of quality measure, ensuring the validity of year-to-year comparisons.

We collected data in four categories of failure dollars:

- *Internal quality incidents,* defined as the costs related to correcting any product defect caught prior to shipping the product, including all labor and materials involved in reworking the product and any materials wasted.

- *Scrap/waste* includes chemical waste costs and materials scrapped due to defects.

- *Customer complaints/recalls* are all costs involved in resolving a customer complaint or recall, including product replacement costs, claims, shipping costs, and labor costs.

- *Product destroyed in field/warranty* is the cost of the deductions our distributors take for product returned by their customers.

3. Analyze the Data. We reviewed data in several stages, making monthly, quarterly, yearly, and year-to-year comparisons. By examining first each of these four categories and then the types of problems within each category, we conducted Pareto analyses (see Figure B.2) to reveal where we were making the most progress and where we should focus ongoing efforts.

4. Improve the Results. As Figure B.2 shows, total failure dollars decreased from 0.70 percent of sales to 0.21 percent of sales. This amounted to a savings of hundreds of thousands of dollars for CRC Industries.

Merely tracking cost of quality could not in itself bring the results we were seeking. With cost of quality as a driver, several key initiatives contributed to our improved results:

- *ISO 9001:2000* certification, achieved in 1996, laid the foundation for our quality system. When we make changes to a process, we update documentation—including procedures, checklists, and instructions—to assure consistency and compliance.

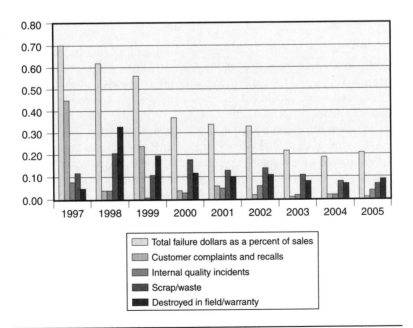

Figure B.2 Pareto chart comparing types of failure dollars.

As part of meeting ISO 9001:2000 requirements, we established quarterly management reviews, which include a review of quality incidents and customer complaints and the related cost of quality data. These reviews give upper management a better understanding of the issues so they can authorize appropriate improvement initiatives.

• *Root cause analysis* sessions have been key in reducing failure costs related to internal incidents and customer complaints. Every employee has received basic training in the relevant techniques needed for these sessions.

The director of quality systems facilitates problem-solving meetings to develop corrective and preventive actions for all significant quality incidents. These meetings involve production operators, supervisors, mixers, shippers, buyers, suppliers, and managers as needed to resolve the problem.

As appropriate, we use techniques like "ask why five times," fishbone analysis, and process mapping to uncover the root cause of the problem. Immediately following the session, we put a series of action items in place. In cases of longer-term projects involving capital approval or training, we add the action items to a pending list. Sometimes, forming an improvement team to work over several weeks or months on improving a process is necessary. Action items and improvement teams' progress are tracked and reviewed at the quarterly management reviews.

• We use our *quality incident database* to track quality incidents that we catch and correct prior to shipping product. The causes are categorized based on the "four M's": specification errors (methods), operator/mixer errors (manpower), equipment problems (machinery), and problems with supplier-provided materials (materials). Costs are also tracked in the database and the information is used in the cost of quality metric.

All of these data feed our root cause analysis sessions as appropriate. We provide some data to suppliers on an annual basis as part of their formal supplier evaluation. A summary of the information is also presented at quarterly management reviews, and improvement teams are authorized as needed based on these data.

• Our *customer complaint database* allows us to collect data and analyze trends in product complaints from our customers. Prior to the database, identifying a problem took much longer since several customers could call in to several different customer service representatives. Each call was viewed as an isolated problem. While we took immediate corrective action with the customer, such as replacing product or issuing credit, we did not identify patterns and thus could not take preventive measures.

With the database, we can consolidate information and use it to identify and correct a recurring problem much faster. We also can track the costs related to each complaint. Customer complaint data are summarized and reported to all employees monthly. The database is also reviewed for trends quarterly and yearly. Pareto analysis of the data allows the management team to select projects that further contribute to a reduction in failure dollars.

CRC Industries' Continuing Commitment to Quality

As our key initiatives work together toward improving cost of quality results, we have witnessed a synergistic effect that facilitates continuous improvement throughout CRC. We can directly or indirectly link cost of quality improvements to other improvements, including, as Table B.1 details, shipping error reductions, customer service order entry error reductions, productivity increases, hazardous waste reduction, and increased profitability.

Order entry and shipment accuracy are directly tied to cost of quality, as each error adds $100 to overall failure dollars. Although improvements of 0.6 percent and 1.0 percent may appear to be minimal, our order entry accuracy was already over 99 percent at the start of our cost of quality project, and our order shipment accuracy was only slightly under 99 percent. These gains therefore brought our accuracy rates even closer to 100 percent.

Hazardous waste costs are also included in our cost of quality failure dollars. Part of the overall cost of quality gains we have made can be

Table B.1   Other progress concurrent with cost of quality improvement.

Metric	Percent improvement since tracking started
Directly related:	
Order entry accuracy	0.6%
Order shipment accuracy	1.0%
Hazardous waste reduction	50%
Indirectly related:	
Orders shipped complete and on time	20%
Productivity	65%
Profit per compensation dollar	3%

attributed to our reduction of hazardous waste by 50 percent over a five-year period.

Improvements in other areas came as part of the overall continuous improvement mind-set at CRC Industries. Results like our 65 percent improvement in productivity and 20 percent improvement in orders shipped complete and on time, for instance, stemmed from a deliberate focus on improving our products and services. However, our cost of quality progress also played a role, at least indirectly, adding momentum to our ongoing efforts to meet and exceed customer requirements.

Endnotes

Chapter 1

1. J. M. Juran and A. B. Godfrey, *Juran's Quality Handbook,* 5th ed. (New York: McGraw-Hill, 1999).
2. ASQ Quality Costs Committee, *Principles of Quality Costs: Principles, Implementation, and Use,* 3rd ed., J. Campanella, editor (Milwaukee: ASQ Quality Press, 1999).
3. Ibid.
4. Ibid.
5. T. Ohno, *Workplace Management,* translated by A. P. Dillon (Cambridge, MA: Productivity Press, 1988).

Chapter 2

1. S. Rodchua, "Quality Costs and Manufacturing Size in the Manufacturing Industry: A Survey Research," Unpublished doctoral dissertation (Indiana State University, 2005). (Dr. Rodchua is currently at the University of Central Missouri, Warrensburg, Missouri 64093.)
2. M. Jordan, *QuoteDB* (May 4, 2007). http://www.quotedb.com/authors/michael-jordan.
3. B. W. Tuckman, "Developmental Sequence in Small Groups." *Psychological Bulletin* 63 (1965): 384–99.

Chapter 5

1. Cokins, G. "Measuring the Cost of Quality for Management," *Quality Progress* 39, no. 9 (September 2006).

Appendix A

1. The material in Appendix A is taken from ASQ Quality Costs Committee, *Principles of Quality Costs: Principles, Implementation, and Use,* 3rd ed., J. Campanella, editor (Milwaukee: ASQ Quality Press, 1999).

Appendix B

1. The material in Appendix B is taken from ASQC Quality Costs Committee, *Quality Costs: Ideas and Applications,* Vol. 2, J. Campanella, editor (Milwaukee: ASQC Quality Press, 1989).
2. ASQ Quality Costs Committee, *Principles of Quality Costs: Principles, Implementation, and Use,* 3rd ed., J. Campanella, editor (Milwaukee: ASQ Quality Press, 1999).

Bibliography

American Society for Quality. "The Cost of Poor Quality." ASQ Web site webinar. This webinar is presented periodically by ASQ. http://www.asq.org/webinars/cost-of-poor-quality.html.

ASQ Quality Costs Committee. *Principles of Quality Costs: Principles, Implementation, and Use,* Third Edition. J. Campanella, editor. Milwaukee: ASQ Quality Press, 1999.

ASQC Quality Costs Committee. *Quality Costs: Ideas and Applications*, Volume 2. J. Campanella, editor. Milwaukee: ASQC Quality Press, 1989.

Atkinson, R., C. Ittner, and J. Hamburg. *Linking Quality to Profits: Quality-Based Cost Management.* Milwaukee: ASQ Quality Press, 1994.

Cokins, G. "Measuring the Cost of Quality for Management," *Quality Progress* 39, no. 9 (September 2006).

Donovan, S. *Using Cost of Quality to Improve Business Results.* Milwaukee: ASQ Quality Press, 2006. http://www.asq.org/economic-case/markets/pdf/donovan-case-study.pdf.

Feigenbaum, A. V. *Total Quality Control.* New York: McGraw-Hill, 1961.

Jordan, M. *QuoteDB.* http://www.quotedb.com/authors/michael-jordan. May 4, 2007.

Juran, J. M., and A. B. Godfrey. *Juran's Quality Handbook,* Fifth Edition. New York: McGraw-Hill, 1999.

Ohno, T. *Workplace Management.* Translated by A. P. Dillon. Cambridge, MA: Productivity Press, 1988.

Rodchua, S. "Quality Costs and Manufacturing Size in the Manufacturing Industry: A Survey Research." Unpublished doctoral dissertation. Indiana State University, 2005. (Dr. Rodchua is currently at the University of Central Missouri, Warrensburg, Missouri 64093.)

Tuckman, B. W. "Developmental Sequence in Small Groups." *Psychological Bulletin* 63 (1965).

Index

A

accounting systems
 loss valuation, 78–79
 and quality cost systems, 8–9, 15,
  39–40, 65–66
 repurposing, 44–46
 role in sustaining cost of quality
  program, 80
appraisal costs, 4
 evaluating, 22
 examples, 83–85
automation, data, 51–52

B

bases, and ratios, 10–13
behavior modification, and quality
 cost systems, 9–10
blame, removing, 74
budget accounts, as source for quality
 costs, 53–57
burning platform, 26

C

case studies (Appendix B)
 #1—quality costs in a bank,
  89–91
 #2—using cost of quality to
  improve business results,
  91–98
cause identification, 20–22
change
 organizational, approaches to,
  32–33
 why of, 31
chargeback systems
 drawbacks of, 75–77
 in quality cost reporting, 61–62
Cokins, Gary, 63
comfort zone, 32
common cause errors, 74
Continental Illinois National Bank
  and Trust Company of Chicago,
  case study, 89–91
controller, benefits of controlling
  quality cost program, 15